July 18, 2000

to Jan,

A good friend to the whole Bickham family. I hope you enjoy this trip down memory lane.

Warmest wishes,

Beverly Bickham

Back Then

A Memoir of Childhood

by Beverly Beckham

"Back Then" is published and printed by Host Communications,
904 North Broadway, Lexington, Kentucky 40505.

W. James Host, Publisher
Mark Coyle, President
Craig Baroncelli, Senior Vice President/Publishing
Dave Mrvos, Vice President/Distribution

Edited by Pat Henderson
Designed by Dana Bart

ISBN: 1-57640-056-5

To order additional copies, contact Host Communications at
800.313.4678 or go to www.beverlybeckham.com

"What I do not put in words on a page will be erased by time." — Isabel Allende

In Memory of Mama and Aunt Lorraine

Acknowledgements

*W*riting is a solitary act. You write alone, one word at a time. Sometimes the words race along like marathon runners and sometimes they get bogged down like old soldiers in combat boots. You write anyway. You write when it's easy and you write when it's hard. You stick with it and you work at it and eventually a kind of alchemy happens. Words become moments, feelings, thoughts, images. Anaïs Nin said, "We write to taste life twice, in the moment and in retrospection." I write to get it right, because the second taste of life is somehow sweeter.

Writing is a solitary act. But publishing the written word is not. This book was no exception. My thanks to all the people who encouraged me, who said, "This is your story, yes, but it's my story, too. You brought back moments of my childhood I thought I had forgotten."

My thanks to Zelda Fischer who was the first to believe in this book; to Alan Eisner who led me to Zelda; to my editor Shelly Cohen who has taught me over the years that less is more; to my husband Bruce for his steadfast support; to my children Rob, Lauren and Julie who were the first to read the rough draft; to Xena Duff Sanchez and Katherine DelCupolo who were the last and whose encouraging words ("You cannot stick this one in a drawer!") are the reason I decided to have it published; to Beth Erickson for always listening; and to Pat Henderson who gently guided me through the difficult publishing process.

Thanks also to Ann Marie Tantillo and Helen Butler for their help with the school photos. And to Terry Kemp at the Canton Post Office for always having a nice word to say.

My special thanks to my parents who gave me the childhood I write about and to Pat and Jim Host who have given me the means to share it.

Table of Contents

Prologue

ou piece it together. That's all you can do. You read old letters, listen to war songs, watch black-and-white movies and study photographs. You close your eyes, and after a while the pieces begin to talk. The words are whispers at first. Sighs. Syllables. Fragments of conversation.

"You're beautiful," says a tall man with dark, curly hair to a woman filmed in midstep.

I am holding a black-and-white picture of my mother taken just outside the bathroom of the house we lived in until I was seven. She is in her nightgown, her face scrubbed, her hair in pin-curls, caught off-guard by my father, the cameraman, who must have been waiting in the hall to get this shot.

In the kitchen a radio plays, making a tinny, old-fashioned sound. Notes fill the small apartment and flutter down the hall. My mother is smiling.

"You're beautiful even with those things in your hair," my father says, backing up, placing the camera on the kitchen table. The camera tips, and the shutter hits the red tabletop. But my father doesn't hear or doesn't care. He walks over to my mother, slips his hand around her waist and leads her into the kitchen, where he takes her in his arms. She sighs, and their cheeks touch as they dance on the worn, linoleum floor, she in her slippers, pink and open-toed, and he in shiny police boots.

My mother sings with the music. "I'm a little lamb who's lost in the wood. I know I could always be good, to one who'll watch over me."

"I love you, Dot," my father whispers.

"I love you, too," my mother murmurs back.

I hang on to this moment. I need to believe in it. I need to believe that this night is real, that once upon a time my parents were happy and crazy in love. Before babies who died and businesses that failed and dreams that dissolved like flowers gone to seed.

"They never got along that way," Lorraine, my

mother's younger sister, tells me. "Your mother would have yelled at him for taking that picture. Look at her. She looks terrible. No makeup. An old nightgown. She was always so careful about her appearance."

She was.

So what do I believe? The picture? The whispers that fill my head? The song? My memories of that moment? Or someone else's?

To piece a life together involves inventing — snippets of conversation here, a bit of dialogue there. Transposing and transgressing and transcending. Adding sounds and scents and sentiment. Is that a sparkle in my mother's eye, or is it a tear? Did someone tell her to smile for the camera, or was she smiling before the camera clicked.

You never really know. All you can do is imagine.

Bride and Groom

I imagine their wedding day, Sunday, August 18, 1946. They were married at St. Patrick's Church in Somerville, Massachusetts, at three in the afternoon. My mother borrowed her wedding gown. My grandfather gave her away. See? There he is in the picture, standing next to her.

But he wasn't in her life. I know this. He walked away years before.

"Where's Pa?" she asks her mother. "Gone," my grandmother says. My mother doesn't ask where. She knows better. He's been gone before: for a few weeks, a month, six months. He always comes back.

He doesn't this time. They move from their house in Haverhill, a great big place with trees, a lawn and a back yard, where they have lived for a year-and-a-half, where Pa has worked steadily, where they have all been happy. They move back to Somerville, back to the city, first to Hampshire Street to a small flat, then to Magnolia Avenue — a grand name, but the street is not. The sidewalks are cracked and the trees are leafless. There are no back yards, only more three-deckers just like theirs.

My grandmother gets a job as a waitress in a bar. My mother quits school and gets a job as a cashier at the A&P. My mother is sixteen. She is tall and lanky, no flesh on her bones. Her hair is dark blonde and straight, but she curls it every night with bobby pins. She makes spit curls. That's what you call them. You put spit on your finger — only she uses water — and you twirl the hair around your finger and fasten the curl with a bobby pin. You do this again and again until your head is covered with bobby pins. Then you take a scarf and wrap it around your head.

When it rains my mother's curls disappear like snow in the sun. She thinks she is ugly with straight hair, but she isn't. She could never be ugly. She has great blue eyes that stop you dead in your tracks — they're what you notice first. People tell her — even shoppers at the

A&P — that she has beautiful eyes.

Her hair is curly in her wedding picture. The day is warm, dry and cloudless. My mother smiles for the camera, but her smile is shy and strained. "Hold still. Everyone look at me. Cheeeese." That's what you hear when you look at the photo.

You hear my grandfather, too, wheezing a smoker's wheeze, and you can almost smell his breath, a strong barroom smell. Above it you hear the steady, rapid beating of my father's heart.

He is a boy in the picture, newly scrubbed, in a tuxedo. He doesn't look as if he has only recently returned from war. He doesn't look as if he has followed General Eisenhower across two continents. He is twenty-four. He is happy. He has won a prize: my mother.

My father's smile is wide and bright, his right hand hanging loosely at his side, his left tucked tenderly around my mother's waist. You can't see his left hand, but you know it's there. You can almost feel it memorizing her, all silk, satin and lace, absorbing her like a blotter absorbs ink.

Mary Andrews is the only other female in the picture. She is my mother's best friend. Her hair is curly like my mother's. She wears a veil, too, and holds a bouquet every bit as big as the bride's. She has dark hair like my Aunt Lorraine's and lips as red as Lorraine's, too. But her lips are pursed, as if she is saying, "Ooh," as if the cameraman has just said something she doesn't like.

The man seated beside her is my Uncle Billy, my mother's older brother. I don't know my Uncle Billy. He's just a photograph in my grandmother's parlor, a name on a Christmas card. He is an old man who comes to visit my mother years later when she is in a hospital. I never know this young Uncle Billy. He is a stranger.

There is another stranger on the other side of the picture: my father's best man, Johnny Ferrara. I ask my father, "Who is that man?" He says, "That's Johnny Ferrara. He used to live on Windsor Street. We grew up together. He was my best friend."

Uncle Jimmy, my father's older brother, stands behind Johnny Ferrara and next to my father. I like my Uncle Jimmy. He says things like, "A clean ship is a happy ship." When he wants you to stop what you're doing and come to him, he says, "All hands on deck." That's Navy talk, my mother tells me. Uncle Jimmy is in the Navy. That's why he wears a uniform. He is married to Laura. I don't call her Aunt Laura. But I call Uncle Jimmy's next wife Aunt Fran.

Uncle Jimmy isn't smiling in the wedding picture. The whole wedding party looks grim except for the bride and groom. So I focus on them. I will them out of the picture, out of the photographer's pose, and set them down in the church at the altar where they are taking their vows.

And I imagine.

The afternoon light plays on the stained glass windows, setting Jesus aglow. A fly buzzes. A siren wails in the distance. The bride, my mother, is talking in a whisper into my father's eyes. She is promising to love, honor and cherish him forever. Johnny Ferrara hands my father the ring. Between his fingers the wedding ring looks small. My father slips it onto my mother's finger. She looks down at it, then up at him. The church is suddenly silent: no street noise, no coughs, no whispers. The priest says, "I now pronounce you man and wife." My mother and father turn and step off the altar. Then they kiss. An organ plays. The church doors swing open.

Now they are outside in the sunlight, well-wishers congratulating them, kids in the neighborhood pausing on their bikes to stare at them, Uncle Jimmy patting my father's back. Big Nana is there in her Sunday best: a navy dress buttoned down the front, thick black shoes and a small black hat. Little Nana is wearing flowers: red ones all over her dress, a pink one in her hair, a white one pinned to her shoulder. She is dabbing at her eyes with a hankie. Her fingernails match her lips. Her lips match her hair. She is Technicolor next to black and white.

"Give me a kiss, sweetie," Little Nana says to my father, then plants her lips on his cheek where they leave their mark. She takes my mother's hand. She looks at the wedding ring. Her eyes grow moist. "Mrs. Curtin," she says with a sigh. Then she hugs my mother.

The reception is at a hotel. It is a small celebration, just the wedding party and a few relatives. "We sat at a table and nobody talked," my father says.

"If I'd been there I could tell you everything. But they shipped me off to camp and got married while I was away," Aunt Lorraine fumes. "I never went to camp in my life. Camp was for rich kids. But suddenly there was your grandmother buying me shorts and T-shirts and washing them so they wouldn't look new, and shelling out money for sneakers, and putting me on a bus and saying, 'See you in two weeks.' When I came back Dorothy was gone. 'Where is she?' I asked. 'Married,' my mother said. And that was that. No one ever said why I wasn't invited, and I never asked."

Why wasn't Lorraine at your wedding, I ask my father fifty years later? "Because she was real troublesome in those days," he tells me.

"She was eleven," I say.

He shrugs. "What difference does it make. It was a long time ago. Why do you care?"

Why do I care?

I am five, and all the time, any time I can, I tell people I was at my mother's wedding. I announce this at the bakery where my mother buys my father hermits and black-and-whites. I yell it out at the bank, where a teller raises her eyes and my mother blushes. I tell the butcher, the man who runs the flower shop and Miss Bates, my dancing teacher.

"No you weren't," my mother repeats again and again. "You were at Mary Andrews' wedding. That's the wedding you saw. I was a bridesmaid. I wore a pretty white dress and a veil, and I rode in a shiny black car, but Mary Andrews was the bride, not me."

Her words cannot dissuade me. I am five and I am convinced I was there in the church as my mother took her vows. I watch her walking down the aisle. I see her kneel in prayer. I listen to her say I do. I wave as she is walking back down the aisle. She waves back, a quick bend of her fingers, and then she winks right at me. "That's my mother!" I say inside my head.

"Why don't you remember, Mama? I was there. Why do you say I wasn't? Why won't you believe me?"

What to believe?

My parents spend their honeymoon in Atlantic City. They drive there in my father's blue DeSoto convertible. It's an old car but new to him, polished and buffed so that you can see yourself in its hood. The top is down, and the sun beats on them. With every mile the sun burns hotter, the air gets thicker and they grow warmer, until they are like two fancy cakes left in the heat, their icing melted.

My father wears a long-sleeve white shirt and a tie, loosened at the neck. His armpits are wet. Sweat beads on his forehead and upper lip. My mother's pale orchid dress is stained at the back. Both are tired from the drive, wilted from the heat, but still they hold hands.

They stop in New York City for a night and check into a hotel on 49th Street. A porter takes their luggage. A clerk, a balding Irish man in his forties, smiles at them. "You're on your honeymoon?" he says knowingly. My father nods. "Well, you'll not be wanting a room with twin beds, then." My mother's cheeks turn pink.

Their room is small, on the fourteenth floor. "What happened to thirteen?" my mother asks in the elevator. The bellman doesn't answer. My father, a man of the world who has been to Italy and France, explains.

"So the fourteenth is really the thirteenth?" my mother says. "And they're just not calling it that?"

My father grins at her.

There is one small window in their room. My mother opens it and peers down at the street at the traffic. She reads the billboards, listens to the city sounds and feels the city heat. It is heavy still, though it is almost evening, though the buildings are pink and purple and it should be cool, cooler than this. She runs water for a bath. She removes her orchid dress and hangs it on the hook at the back of the door. She takes off her bra and panties and washes them in the bathroom sink before she slips into the tub.

My father sits on the bed with the chenille spread and fiddles with the radio until he finds a station he likes. Now soft music fills the room. My father takes off his tie and shoes, props up the pillows, leans back, stretches out and closes his eyes.

Later they dress in their honeymoon clothes and go out on the town. They drink champagne and dance on the rooftop of the Hotel Astor to the Kay Kaiser Band. "This one's for the honeymooners," Kay Kaiser says and plays "Sentimental Journey." My mother and father stay on the dance floor until the band stops playing. Then they walk to Times Square and have breakfast.

It's a new day when they go back to their hotel room. The buildings are pink again, the sun now rising. They sleep until just before checkout, which is at noon. Then they pack their bags and head for Atlantic City.

The Newlyweds

The Honeymooners

There. See her? She is on a chaise lounge on the Boardwalk, in full makeup, wearing earrings and a black and white sundress. But this is impossible. There are no pictures recording this. The honeymooners do not own a camera. They don't own much more than what is in their suitcases.

They spend their days on the Boardwalk under a wide umbrella because my father had malaria in the war and too much sun bothers him. My mother loves the sun but sits under the umbrella with him. Early morning and late in the day they walk along the beach, my father in long pants and shoes, my mother in a sundress and barefoot. At noon after lunch, when the sun is strongest, they take a nap. Every night after dinner, when the sun has set, they see a show, then dance themselves into the next day.

My mother sings as she dances. She knows the words to every song. My father loves this about her. Her singing makes him happy. One night, very late, when the dance floor is almost empty, the bandleader asks if she wants to come up and sing along. She has done this before. She won ten dollars in a contest just six months ago in a movie theater in Somerville. She bought my father a pair of shoes with half her winnings. The other half she gave to her mother. This night she approaches the mike, adjusts it and, turning to my father, sings their wedding song. "Gonna take a sentimental journey, gonna set my heart at ease. Gonna make a sentimental journey to renew old memories."

My father is six feet going on ten feet tall. He is Paul Bunyan. The few people remaining in the club burst into applause. Their eyes tell him he's a lucky man. "More! More!" they chime, begging my mother to continue. But she declines, says thank you, takes my father's arm and retreats to their room.

Five days later they are back in Cambridge, back to work, back to my father's house where they live with my father's mother. They sleep upstairs in a room next to Little Nana. My mother hears Little Nana turning the pages of the paperback books she reads late into the night. She hears her chewing her Chiclets, lighting her cigarettes and sighing. My grandmother hears my mother giggling.

My father works at Lewis and Shepard in Watertown. He makes the cranes that lift furniture. My mother works at Raytheon on an assembly line. Nine to five feels like forever. Nights feel like forever, too, at the kitchen table, eating dinner, making small talk — what did you do all day? All the days feel the same, sitting in the parlor listening to the news about Nazi war criminals, killing time until bedtime, then lying there whispering, smiling, content until dawn.

They move out before I am born. My mother and grandmother have an argument. My mother packs her honeymoon bag, lugs it to the park and sits on a bench wondering what she is going to do. My father comes home from work and finds her gone.

"What happened, Ma?"

"She left. She's temperamental. Just up and left. I never said a word, though I wanted to. Let me make you a cup of tea."

My father doesn't want tea. He wants my mother. He goes searching for her. It's only 5:30, but it is December, cold and midnight dark. He finds my mother on the bench where they always sit, where he asked her to marry him.

"Let's go back," he says.

"No. I'm never going back."

"Then where will we go?"

My mother shrugs.

"It's either my mother's or yours. We don't have much choice. We can't sleep here," my father says.

They walk over to Big Nana's and ring the bell. Lorraine answers. My grandmother is at work. When she comes home it is 2 a.m. and my mother and father are asleep in my mother's room. The next morning my grandmother wakes them. "If you're staying with me, you're going to have to live by my rules," she announces. "Dorothy, get up and make breakfast. And you?" she says turning to my father, "How do you like your eggs?"

•   •   •   •

I am born in February while my father is at work. "Where's Dot?" he asks when he comes home at night. It is 5:30. The table is set. Dinner is cooking. Lorraine is in the kitchen helping her mother.

"She had to run an errand," my grandmother tells him.

They sit at the table. They eat beef stew and bread. My grandmother talks about some man at the bar who has just left his wife or who's just lost his job or who just fell off the wagon. Lorraine anticipates the fireworks that are going to explode when my grandmother finally gets around to telling my father that he has a child.

My father keeps glancing at his watch and looking at the door. He doesn't have a clue about me because I am not due for weeks.

"Have some pie," my grandmother says, clearing the plates. She cuts the pie, apple, which is my father's favorite. She pours the coffee. "Milk? Sugar?" It is 6:10, 6:20. My father lights a cigarette.

"Now I'll tell you," my grandmother says when the cigarette has been stubbed out. "Dorothy is in the hospital. She had the baby this afternoon."

Lorraine says she has never seen anyone so angry as my father at that minute. He was so mad that he turned blue. He was so mad that he couldn't speak. He pounded his fist on the table, threw back his chair, grabbed his coat and slammed the door behind him.

I had been born shortly after noon. My mother screamed for a doctor. "The baby's coming. Won't someone help me?" But no one did. I had made my appearance by the time the doctor sauntered in the door. They took me away and put me in an incubator. They told my mother that I was very small and very weak. They shook their heads when they talked about me.

My mother waited for my father to arrive. Surely her mother called his work and told him what had happened. Where was he? Why wasn't he here? He didn't arrive until just before 7 p.m. "I'm sorry," he said, rushing past a row of women. "She never told me. I didn't know." He cried when he saw my mother, wan and red-eyed, and he cried harder when he laid eyes on me. I looked like a bird, he said. A poor, sick, little bird. A priest came. My mother sobbed. You'll have others. Try to get some sleep now. You have to be strong.

Two days, three days, and I am still alive — yellow and scrawny like an Easter chicken just hatched, but alive, blessed be God. Big Nana takes a cab to the hospital to bring my mother home. I cannot go home, the hospital tells her. I have to stay in the incubator.

"Bullshit," my grandmother says. "You'll give me that baby right now."

"That's impossible, Mrs. Haley. That baby is sick and needs to stay here."

"Bullshit," my grandmother repeats. "You give me that child now."

My mother has to sign a paper. The doctors warn her that she is doing a terrible thing. My grandmother says, "Hurry up, Dorothy. The meter's running." My grandmother carries me home, lights the oven, opens the door and places me in a bureau drawer lined with blankets in front of the oven. She boils water on the stove, buckets of it, so that the room is steamy like a July day.

I don't die. My grandmother puts honey in my milk and sugar in my water and feeds me every two hours. My mother says, "I want to feed her." But my grandmother says, "No. You do the laundry. You cook the dinner. You go to the store and get the evaporated milk, and you sterilize the bottles and wash the diapers. Then you should rest. You don't want to get rundown. I'll take care of the baby.

"She never let me near you," my mother says when I am older. "Between your grandmother and Lorraine, I never stood a chance."

Beverly Beckham

Mama and me

Quick as a Flash

We move to our own place, to the projects. My grandmother says, "Why are you going? All you'll meet is riff-raff there." Lorraine holds me and cries.

My mother buys a big braided rug. It's brown and red, the only rug in the small flat. I have a toy carpet sweeper. I clean the rug every day.

We get a dog. His name is Pal. I call him my pal. Pal can go outside and play, but I cannot. Pal can swim in the lake where I live, but I cannot.

"It is not a lake," my father tells me. "It is just a big hole full of dirty, smelly water. I don't want you near it, not ever. Do you understand?"

One day when my mother is lying down, I sneak out the door and run to the lake. I take off my shoes, then my socks. I take off my shorts, then my shirt. I am in the water. I am walking in the water, splashing, playing. I am all alone. Even Pal is somewhere else.

Then Mona walks by, my mother's new friend who lives upstairs. All of sudden Mona is screaming, "What are you doing out there? Get out of that water right now!" And then my mother appears. I feel her before I see her, dragging me out of the lake, slapping my bottom, yelling at me, "Didn't your father tell you never to go near the water? Didn't I tell you? Don't you know what could have happened to you?"

I don't know. All I know is that my mother never yells at me and has never before gone racing across the pavement barefoot and in her bathrobe. My mother always wears heels, a dress and fresh lipstick. She pulls me into the house. She wraps a towel around me and gets me clean clothes. She yells at me and makes me tea. She hugs me, gives me a cookie and makes me promise that I will never, ever do anything like this again.

Then my father comes home. He sits me on his lap and tells me that I am a very bad girl and that I frightened my mother. He tells me that if I ever go near that water again I won't be able to sit down for a week.

"Do you understand me?" he says.

This time I really do understand. I never go near that water again.

• • • •

My father buys me a tricycle. It is red and has a black seat. I ride it around the kitchen and over the rug. I want to ride it outside, but my mother says, "No. It's too dangerous. There are too many cars."

Pal chases cars. He gets in fights almost every day. He fights with cats and brings them home. He drags them into the house and my mother chases both him and them out with a broom. Pal fights with little dogs and makes them run across the street. He growls at the ragman, too, and would fight him if he could. I don't blame him. I don't like the ragman. He knocks on our door and I hide. My mother says, "Beverly, come here." I don't. I close my eyes because the ragman is thin and has yellow teeth and a dirty beard. I hold my breath because he smells like the rags my mother throws away. I hide behind the couch and make myself invisible until he leaves.

One day Pal fights with a big dog, comes home with a hole in his side and bleeds all over my mother's braided rug. She cries. I think that it's because her rug is stained, so I get my carpet sweeper and try to rub out the blood. But it spreads everywhere.

My father comes home and puts Pal in the car.

"Where are you going?"

"I'm taking Pal to the doctor," my father says.

"Can I come?"

"No, you stay here with your mother."

A long time goes by, and my father returns without Pal. My mother cries and cries and throws away the braided rug. She says she will never get another dog. She cannot go through this again.

But then one day my father brings home a puppy. The puppy is cute, soft and little. And though we miss Pal — no one could take Pal's place — we like this dog. I hold him in my arms. "Can we keep him, Mama?" I hand him to her. I know she is thinking about Pal and the hole in his side. I am thinking about Pal, too. But this other dog is licking my face and making me giggle. My mother says to my father, "What should we call him?" My father says, "How about Buttons?" and Buttons it is. Buttons stays and sleeps in my room that night.

• • • •

There's Buttons, big now; I am big, too. I am four and it is summer, a hot day. The laundry is wet and cool. I stand outside with my mother, between the sheets and shirts, and hand her clothespins as she pins more towels on the line.

Aunt Lorraine is here, too. My mother thinks that Lorraine has come to visit her and to show off her new camera. But I know that she has come to visit me. Sometimes, after she spends time at our house, sitting at the kitchen table drinking coffee and making my mother laugh, Lorraine takes me home with her to Big Nana's house. Big Nana lives above the Shamrock Cafe, the place where she works. She says that it's convenient. She says that all she has to do is walk down a flight of stairs to get where she has to be. She doesn't have to take a bus across town anymore. She likes her new flat.

I like it, too. I like the big black stove in the kitchen and the open porch just off the kitchen where my grandmother lets me feed the birds. And I like sitting on the chair next to the window in my grandmother's bedroom and watching her dress for work. A sign flashes outside the window. I sound it out: din-ner. I think it says dinner, because that's what people do there — they eat. But Lorraine says it's dine-er and that dine is just a fancy word for eating. "It's not a fancy place, though," I say, and my grandmother and Lorraine laugh.

My grandmother dresses in white, like a nurse, to pour people beers. She wears a white dress, a white apron and white shoes with great thick white soles. My mother says

Beverly Beckham

that she's a lot like a nurse, always trying to fix everyone's troubles, always carrying other people's problems
around like they're hers.

Aunt Lorraine takes me to Big Nana's after she takes
my picture with her new camera. Big Nana is walking
down the stairs dressed for work. She sees me, smiles,
kisses my cheek and tucks a quarter into my hand. "For
luck," she says.

"I want you to iron tonight," she says to Lorraine.

"Yes, Ma."

"And clean up the kitchen after you cook."

"I will, Ma."

"And I don't want you keeping that child out late
hanging around the five-and-ten, do you hear?"

"I hear, Ma."

Lorraine told me one day when we were in the five-
and-ten that my grandmother named her after a comb.
Lorraine was brushing her hair, trying on lipstick and
dabbing nail polish on me, opening the bottles, though
you're not supposed to. Joe the key man was across the
aisle watching her. She pretended that she didn't know
he was watching and started talking about being named
after a comb and how the name Lorraine was printed
right on it. "Right here," she said, pointing to the plastic
top. I thought this was just a made-up story until I asked
my grandmother later and she said, "No, it's true." Then
she turned to Lorraine and said, "I hope you didn't drag
her to the five-and-ten just so you could flirt with that
moron." Lorraine's whole face got as red as her lips; she
glared at Big Nana, and I thought she was going to yell
at her. But she didn't.

Now every time anyone mentions the five-and-ten I
think of Lorraine and the comb, I think how funny it
would be if the comb was called Lucy or Cecile. Imagine. Aunt Lucy or Aunt Cecile.

•   •   •   •

We are walking down the street, and I am with my

favorite person in the whole world besides my mother and father. I am carrying a red flower that the florist, a man with dark, shiny hair, gave me. "One for the little girl and one for the beautiful lady," he said to my aunt. My stomach is full because Lorraine and I have just come from the five-and-ten where I had a vanilla milk shake and she had a Coke and a cigarette. We are now on our way home. I am skipping because I am happy; Lorraine is frowning because Joe the key man wasn't working tonight. We are holding hands and I see the bus, our bus, across the street. I drop Lorraine's hand and make a bee-line toward the street. I fly off the sidewalk into the path of a car that slams on its brakes and screeches to a stop, just inches from where I stand.

And Aunt Lorraine, who never raises her voice to me, who says "Yes, Baybo," "Of course" and "Anything you want, honey," spanks me right on the spot. She continues spanking me all the way home.

It is a long, long way because we walk from Central Square to Inman Square. My feet are sore, I'm tired and I'm sad, too, because all the while we're walking my aunt is yelling at me, "You almost got killed. Do you real-ize that? What would I have done? How could I have told your mother? What would she ever do without you!"

I am thinking that Lorraine will never let me sleep over again. She'll never paint my fingernails red or let me sit on the bathtub and watch her powder her face because she hates me now. She hates me because I almost got killed, and what would my mother do without me? And I am sad, so sad, and trying not to cry.

She doesn't tell Big Nana what happened, though. And neither do I. We stop at the barroom because we always stop there. I sit on a stool. Nana gives me a sip of beer, looks at me and says, "Are you all right?" I nod my head and Nana says to Lorraine, "I think she's coming down with something. I want you to take her upstairs and put her to bed."

Lorraine sits at the kitchen table and smokes a cigarette while I change into my pajamas. Then she comes
into the bedroom to tuck me in. She doesn't act as if she
hates me. She kisses me goodnight the way she always
does. Then she says, "I love you, Baybo." But just before
she turns out the light, she looks at me, shakes her head
and says "I don't know how that car missed you. You are
a lucky little girl."

Search for Tomorrow

My mother is taken to the hospital. Aunt Lorraine comes and stays with me.

"What's wrong with Mama?"

"Nothing's wrong.

"Then why is she at the hospital?"

"She won't be there long, honey."

My father comes home from work. He is a police officer now. He sits in his uniform in front of the TV with the sound turned off. My aunt reads the same page of the newspaper over and over. Little Nana stops by. "I'm so sorry," she says, hugging my father.

We pick up my mother the next day. I ride in the front seat of the car. My father is wearing his Sunday clothes, though it's not Sunday. It's a spring day, and the trees are green. He parks in front of the hospital and tells me to sit there and wait for him. He never does this. He never leaves me in the car alone. What if the Gypsies steal me, I want to ask him. But I don't. I sit in the car and look out the window and wait for my mother to appear.

When I see her, I think, there she is. There's Mama! Only then I think — is it? Why isn't she looking at me? Why isn't she running toward me the way she always does? My father is helping her down the steps. He has his arm around her waist, and she is leaning against him. I recognize her shiny shoes and her flowered dress, and that's her face. But she's walking like Big Nana walks up the stairs after working all night. I climb over the front seat and sit in the back. My father opens the door, and my mother slides into the car and says, "Hi, Baybo."

"Hi, Mama."

"Are you all right?"

I nod, but I'm not. I'm confused. Why are your eyes red, Mama? Why are you so sad, I want to ask her. But my father gets in the car and squeezes her hand, and she cries. I sit in the back and don't say anything. I just count telephone poles all the way home.

• • • •

My father takes me for a long drive. Buttons comes, too. I wear pants and a plaid shirt, not a dress, because Mama says to.

"Why didn't Mama come with us?"

"Because she needs her rest," my father says.

We stop at a farm stand and buy peaches. They are big and juicy. My father eats three, I eat two and Buttons eats one. We have a picnic in the woods, and Buttons runs free. No one yells, "Get back here, Buttons. Come, Buttons." The woods are deep and cool. We sit on a picnic bench and eat bologna and cheese sandwiches my father made. There's a lake in the woods, a real lake. I want to swim, but my father says, "No, this lake isn't for swimming." We ride in a boat instead. He lets me row. Buttons sits so still that my father says, "I think that dog is afraid of water."

"I'm not afraid," I tell him.

"You should be," he says.

We play horseshoes. "Why do they call it horseshoes?" I ask.

"Because, see how this is shaped like a horse's shoe?" my father says.

I don't see. I didn't even know that horses wore shoes. My father tells me that they're not real shoes, not the kind of shoes I'm wearing. Then he tells me some cowboy stories. I love cowboy stories, and he does, too.

Before we leave he asks me, "How would you like to plant a tree?"

"A tree? How can we do that?"

"Simple. Go get me that bag of peaches in the car."

I run and get them. "The first thing you have to do," he says, "is eat a peach." The peaches are warm now and even juicer than before. "You have to eat every bit," he tells me. He eats all his oozy, runny fruit, then sucks on the pit until it looks like a walnut. I do the same. "Okay, now we have to find something to dig with," he says. This time he goes to the car, opens the trunk and comes back with a small shovel. "Where do you think we should plant it?"

I look around. We are surrounded by trees. It's all trees, lake and blue sky. How will we ever find our tiny tree in all of this?

We walk to the edge of the lake. My father counts footsteps. He says I can't count mine because my feet are still growing; if I count and then come back some day, the count will be different because my feet will be bigger. "One, two, three," he begins, being careful to walk normally and not take giant steps. "Fifty-one, fifty-two, fifty-three. Fifty-three paces from the lake. What do you think? Can you remember that?"

I nod. He digs. It's not a big hole. I step into it; it's just above my ankle. He pulls his peach pit from his pants pocket and places it in the hole. Then he walks three steps and digs another hole. I put my peach pit in that. We push all the dirt back into the holes, then we walk on it, he says, to pack the dirt down. Now we have to water the trees. So we go back to the lake and fill our Coke bottles with water. We do this again and again — my father says trees need a lot of water to grow.

Buttons lies under a tall Christmas tree and watches us. I want to stay and wait for our trees to grow. I want to sit there and watch them. I think that with all that water those seeds have to do something — maybe even float to the top. My father says it takes a long time for a tree to grow. He says some trees don't grow at all — even when you've done everything right. Sometimes you plant the seed, water it and expect it to grow, and there's no reason it shouldn't. Look at all the trees that used to be just seeds. "But nature's funny like that," he says. "Some seeds die in the ground where you can't even see them."

"Not our tree. Ours will grow."

"I hope so."

My father whistles for Buttons. It's dark, and my mother is still resting when we get home.

Buttons and me

Leave It to Larry

There is music in the house. A piano. Violins. My mother is singing "I have mixed emotions, when it comes to loving you, for I shouldn't love the things you shouldn't do."

The music comes from a wooden box in the parlor. It's a Victrola, my mother tells me. I look, and there's a picture of a dog inside the box. He's white and cute, but he doesn't look like Buttons. Buttons is cuter, I say.

The Victrola isn't at all like the radio. You have to crank a handle to get the Victrola to play, and it doesn't play for long. But my mother likes it. She sings "Because of You" and "Slow Poke" and I sing along with her because I know the words to these songs.

My father comes home. He changes out of his uniform into khaki pants and rolls up the sleeves of a plaid shirt. Then he turns on the TV. He watches "The Range Rider." This is his favorite show. Mine is "Gene Autry." My father says that "Gene Autry" is for girls. I say it is not and my father says it is. My mother says, "Stop teasing her, Larry."

On Sunday, after church, we go for a drive in my father's blue car. My father is in his Sunday suit, and my mother and I are wearing matching dresses. These are our mother-and-daughter dresses. I love my mother-and-daughter dress, because it makes me feel grown up.

It is summer, hot, and the breeze as we drive is hot, too, but it cools us anyway. My mother is in the front seat with her shoes off and her eyes closed. My father's left hand is on the wheel and his right arm is stretched across the back of the seat. I am in the middle of the back seat but on the edge; my chin is resting on my father's arm.

We are on Route 2 in Arlington. "How come you always know where you are, Dad? How come you never get lost?"

"I get lost. I just don't tell you."

The houses on both sides of the road are big, like castles. They have pretty lawns, and some have fences.

Some have porches where people just sit and watch the cars go by.

My father's car is chugging up a big hill. "Come on, baby, come on. You can do it," he is saying in his talking-to-his-car voice. The car stops dead in its tracks. My father pulls up the emergency brake, pumps the clutch, plays with the choke and counts to five. He says, "Come on, sweetheart, come on." But the car just sits there. People start beeping their horns because it's a hot day. The nice thing about going for a drive on a hot day is that you can feel the breeze in your face. Now we've stopped that breeze for all the people behind us, who are sitting still and sweating.

My father says he is going to push the car to the side of the road.

"Let me help, Larry," my mother offers, her eyes open now. But he says, "Not on your life, Dot. You just steer." Some of the people who had been beeping their horns get out of their cars and help my father. Then they get back in their cars and drive away.

It's very hot sitting by the side of the road, and I'm thirsty. My father says, "Don't worry. The police will be by soon." But they're not. So he says, "Wait here." He takes off his suit jacket, rolls up his sleeves and walks down the road.

My mother and I play "I'm-thinking-of-a-word-that-begins-with" while he's gone. But my father is gone so long that we run out of words. So we decide to sing. "You keep me waiting till it's gettin' aggravatin', you're a slow poke. I wait and worry but you never seem to hurry, you're a slow poke." We sing all the verses once, twice, almost three whole times, until my father finally returns in a police cruiser to rescue us.

"Would you like to hear the siren?" the policeman asks. I say, "Would I?" The siren screams, and we go speeding by all the fancy houses and shiny cars. The breeze is so strong now it's like sitting in front of Big

Nana's fan. I feel like Buttons must feel when he sticks his head out the car window. The policeman stops at Howard Johnson's, where my mother works at night when I'm in bed. She disappears inside and returns with ice cream for everyone. The ice cream melts faster than I can eat it and spills on my mother-and-daughter dress. "Don't worry," says my mother, who is sitting in the back seat with me. "It's not chocolate. It'll wash out."

The next Sunday we don't go for a ride after church. We walk back home and sit in the hot apartment. The blue car has died. We're going to have to get a new one.

"How are we going to afford it?" Mama asks.

"I don't know, but I'll figure it out," my father tells her. For weeks he takes the bus to work. I see him walking down the road. Sometimes, in the afternoon or late at night, he gets a ride home. One day he drives home in a new car. "Oh, it's not new, sweetheart. It's older than the other one, but it works. It gets you where you're going. That's what's important," he tells me.

It's a gray car. I think it looks like a big whale, but I love it because the next Sunday it takes us all the way to Revere Beach. There the breeze is so cool that I shiver, and my father sits on the seawall and puts his arm around me.

My father and me

I Led Three Lives

eople say to my mother, "So, she's an only child?" while we're waiting for the butcher to slice the bologna and cheese extra thin because that's the way we like it; or on the street, when my mother runs into someone she used to know.

"You've just got the one? So she's an only child?"

I think being an only child must be a Very Bad Thing, because the ladies frown when they say this. I try to be a good only child. I try to behave when we are walking to the five-and-ten, all the errands finished, a treat on the swirly chairs at the soda fountain my reward for being good. There's Woolworth's just a few steps away. But then someone shouts, "Dot? Dot Haley?" And the someone hurries to my mother and starts talking. My mother talks back, and they talk and talk. I want to tug on her hand or pull on her dress and say, "Mama, let's go now." But I am oh-so-patient for the longest time.

I stare at my shoes: black patent leather. My mother polishes them with Vaseline. I play rich-man, poor-man with the buttons on my coat. I say the alphabet to myself. I sing "Slow Poke" in my head. I don't mean to tug. Mama says, "In a minute, honey, in a minute. Try to be patient." And I try, I do, but I *have* been patient, doesn't she see?

And then the stranger looks at me and says, "Do you have any more children, Dorothy?" and my mother shakes her head no. I know it makes her sad that she doesn't have a baby — because she is always staring into baby carriages the way I stare into penny candy jars. So I tug with an urgency now; I want to get Mama away from this woman who is making her sad.

And that's when the stranger says, "You've just the one? So she's an only child?" And I know that if I'm the only child I need to be a very good only child — there isn't anyone else to show this lady that my mother is a very good mother who deserves to have more babies. But I pull on her dress and tug on her arm anyway until

Mama says to the stranger, "We really must be going." Then she turns, and we walk away.

"I'm sorry, Mama," I say when we are at the soda fountain at the five-and-ten.

"It's not your fault, honey. That one's an old busybody anyway. She'd talk a dog off a meat wagon. I was dying to get away from her. You were just an excuse. Hurry up, now. Drink your milk shake. We have to get home."

As Mama sips coffee and puffs on a Kent cigarette — one with a filter — I wonder if it's true. Is it really and truly not my fault that I am an only child?

I sit on my bed at night and wait for the first star. "Star light, star bright, first star I see tonight. I wish I may, I wish I might, have the wish I wish tonight." I chant this with my fingers and toes crossed, just the way you're supposed to. Then I whisper, "Please, pretty please, dear God, I wish for a baby brother or sister. I don't care which," though I do care. I would rather have a sister any day.

I wish on the first star for weeks and weeks — and still I am an only child. I don't understand why the wishes aren't working.

Mama reads me stories from the Bible. One night she tells me about Moses, about how his mother was a beautiful and rich princess who had everything in the world except a child, and about how one day she was walking along a river bank and baby Moses came floating to her in a basket.

I look in my mother's laundry basket, but all I find under the sheets and towels are clothespins and a bone that Buttons has buried. I think that, maybe, if we had a river in our back yard, then Mama would get a baby. So I start asking the first star for a river, too.

I get out of bed one night. It's winter. It's cold and it's dark, except for the thin light coming from under the door of my parents' room. I hurry past to the bathroom because I really have to go; but on the way back to my bed I pause and hear my father say to Mama, "Jesus

Christ himself was an only child, Dot. You can't keep letting yourself get disappointed like this. It not your fault."

I open their bedroom door.

"Mama?"

She turns to me. Her eyes are red. "Come on in, Baybo."

I climb between my mother and father. The bed is warm, and I slide under the covers where it is even warmer. Did Jesus do this, I wonder? Did Jesus climb into bed between his parents in the middle of the night? I want to ask them and am about to. But my father says, "Go to sleep, the two of you," and shuts off the light.

I never thought about Jesus being an only child before. I like thinking about this. Mama has a statue of Jesus on her bureau. She says we're all supposed to act like Jesus and that we're supposed to pray to him. I wonder if Jesus ever tugged on his mother's dress when she stopped and talked to someone. And I wonder if he felt sorry later.

Mama and me

The Gene Autry Show

We live in a new place now. The lake is gone, and Mona doesn't live upstairs and the ragman no longer knocks at our door. This makes me glad. I have a new room. I wish on a different star. I wish so hard that my face hurts from squeezing my eyes tight. I wish that Buttons would come back. I don't care about a brother or sister anymore. I just want Buttons.

They don't allow pets here, Mama says. Even if Buttons did come back we couldn't keep him. The Cunninghams, who own our house, say no dogs. But I would hide Buttons in my room. I would sleep under the bed with him and take him out for walks late at night when the Cunninghams — who don't like dogs — are sleeping. I would share my food with him and give him all my milk. I wouldn't let anyone know about him or tell him to go away, even if sometimes I didn't feel like playing.

My father took Buttons to a farm. That's what Mama says. He's there with a bunch of other dogs having a grand old time, she says. "Don't worry about him, Baybo. He's happy."

I am not happy. I sit in my room and draw pictures of Buttons, but they don't look like Buttons. Little Nana buys me a stuffed dog. He's big and soft and black and white. I call him Buttons. I fall asleep with my arm around him, but he doesn't bark or lick my face or wag his tail or smell like the outside. He's not a real dog. He's just a toy.

"Can we go visit Buttons at the farm?" I beg. Mama says, "Maybe someday." My father says, "Dot, she can't go visit him." Lorraine comes over and says, "Let's go to the five-and-ten, and you can get a sundae if you want."

I get my coat and hat because it's winter and it's freezing outside. We run to the corner and take the bus to Central Square. I sit on the twirly stool and spin around and around. The sundae comes — hot fudge with marshmallow — and I eat it all. Lorraine says, "There, don't you feel better now?" And I say, "No. I still miss Buttons."

Mama buys me a turtle. I wake up one morning and there he is in a glass bowl in the kitchen next to the bread box. His name is Duffy. I pick up Duffy, and he hides his head; I touch his feet, and he hides those, too; and Duffy turns into a stone in my hand. I put him on the kitchen floor and out come his feet, then out comes his head, then off he goes across the floor. Mama smiles.

"Do you like him, Beverly?"

"I like him, Mama."

"I thought you would."

• • • •

My father comes home from work and announces that he is taking me to a rodeo.

"What's a rodeo, Dad?"

"It's a show where you get to see real cowboys ride real horses and do tricks with ropes."

"Like rope a steer? Like on TV?"

"Like on TV, sweetheart."

Mama buys me a cowgirl outfit, a dark blue skirt with fringe at the bottom and a vest to match. "We'll get you an authentic cowboy hat at the rodeo," my father promises.

The day of the rodeo, Mama boils water on the stove and gives me a Saturday night bath, though it's not Saturday night. My father says that I don't need a bath. "Have you ever been to a rodeo, Dot? Those horses don't exactly smell like rose water, you know."

Mama says she doesn't care what the horses smell like, but she does care how her only daughter smells. I don't have cowboy boots, so I wear my red rain boots instead. "You can pretend they're cowboy boots," my father says.

I have never been to Boston Garden before. I picture a big garden full of trees, flowers and water bubblers, and maybe some swings and a slide. But when we get off the train and my father says, "This is it," it's not like what I imagined at all. It's a building and we go inside, but it's so huge that it feels like outside; and the ceiling is so high and wide that it looks like a sky. There are zillions of people, zillions of children like me, most of them dressed up like cowboys in fringe and hats and bandannas.

"How will we know the real cowboys, Dad?"

"We'll know," he tells me.

We have seats close to the arena — that's the place where the show will be. "See there? That aisle? That's where the cowboys will come from. And see over there? That's where the calves and steers are kept. Keep your eye on those places. You don't want to miss a thing."

"How do you know this, Dad? Have you been to a rodeo before?"

"A long time ago, sweetheart, before you were born."

I try to imagine before I was born. I try to imagine my father as a boy. I wasn't born old, he always says. But though I believe him, I can't imagine him young.

My father buys me a straw cowboy hat that's trimmed with thin red rope and ties under the chin. I put it on and feel just like Gene Autry. He also buys me a holster with a toy gun with caps. "That's better than popcorn and candy, don't you think?"

The lights flash and a voice booms — where is it coming from? — and a man welcomes us to the rodeo. Everyone yells and hollers, and I yell and holler, too. Then when it gets quiet again, the man says, "Starring," and he pauses, "The one and only," and he pauses again, "The incomparable," pause, "The magnificent," pause, "GENE AUTRY."

And Gene Autry appears right on the aisle, right where my father said. I watch and there he is in his almost-white suit and his almost-white hat. He's tipping it and waving it, and he's RIGHT HERE, almost next to me. He's riding Champion, the most beautiful horse in the whole wide world, and he's singing, he's singing TO ME! "I'm back in the saddle again. Out where a friend is a friend."

"It's Gene Autry, Dad! It's Gene Autry!"

And my father laughs and says, "I know, sweetheart.

Surprised?" And I am so surprised that I forget that I am four-and-a-half and getting to be a big girl, much too big to act like a baby in public. I hug my father. I hug him and I kiss him. I tell him he's the best father in the whole wide world and this is the best night ever. I sit in my seat and listen to Gene Autry sing. I watch cowboys I don't know ride bareback, lasso steer, stand on top of horses, jump through fire and dance with their ropes.

And at the end Gene Autry rides down the aisle, back to wherever he came from, and he's singing again and I'm singing too. I'm going to remember this night my whole life, I tell my father. I'm never going to forget, not ever. Not even when I'm all grown up.

The Telltale Clue

Mama says Christmas is right around the corner, so I run and get my coat and hat. Mama says, "Where are you going?" I say, "Outside." She says, "Don't forget your mittens." I grab them but don't put them on.

I fly down the stairs and out the door, and I let it bang. I don't care if the Cunninghams, who don't like noise almost as much as they don't like dogs, yell at me. Christmas is right around the corner, and I have to catch it before it goes marching down the street and out of sight. I can't chase it past the corner; I'm not allowed. I can't follow the winding road to its end or go off my street, ever. I won't be five for two more months. So I can go only to the corner and no farther.

I'm out of breath when I get there and I'm panting — and that's all I hear and see — my loud, cold breath. I look both ways, up the street and down, but nothing's there — not a piece of tinsel, not a note of a song, nothing red or green or shimmery. There's a dirty white car up on the sidewalk, part of an old newspaper in the gutter, empty candy wrappers and smoked cigarettes. But the street is as still and silent as a picture, leafless and gray. Shades are drawn; doors are closed; there's not a soul in sight. If Christmas had just paraded by, wouldn't people have been out on their steps to welcome it? Wouldn't there be a broken ornament, a burned out bulb, candy canes, popcorn, something, a scent in the air, some proof that it had come and gone?

I am not allowed to go any farther than the corner, which bends and winds. Past the corner I could get lost or bad men could grab me. Children disappear every day. My father knows; he's a policeman. He tells me about little girls who disobey their parents, cross the street and get hit by cars; or who talk to strangers, or worse — take candy from them — and fall into a deep sleep never to wake again.

Oh, but I want to look down that road because Mama said Christmas is right around the corner, and Mama doesn't lie. I know, I am sure, that Christmas is marching just out of sight, like my father marched in the spring with all his police friends, carrying the flags, riding horses and banging drums. I know that hundreds of people are hanging out windows and standing on the sidewalks, just like they did then, cheering Christmas on.

I want to cheer, too. I blow on my fingers because they're cold, and I put on my mittens. I think, I won't go far. I'll just go a little way, and if I don't hear anything I'll run right back. I turn the corner. I don't cross the street, though; I stay on the same side. But as I turn, I tell myself that I live at 26 Calvin Street — this is my new address and I don't want to forget.

The wind blows, and a newspaper flies like an old kite. Something in the sewer rattles, and something else howls. I race past the dirty white car — what if there's a bad man inside, lying on the seat, and what if he's been hiding there waiting for a little girl to disobey her parents because he knows that's what little girls do? And what if he grabs me and makes me eat candy, and I fall asleep and never see my mother again?

All the shades are drawn in all the windows, and the doors are closed. The street is empty and silent except for me, my footsteps and my breath and the wind howling. Just a little bit farther. Just go a little bit farther, a voice in my head is saying. Don't be scared. Don't be a baby. Hurry. Run. You're gonna miss it. Christmas won't wait for you.

But another voice, my mother's, soft and pleading, is whispering, what would I ever do without you? What would I do, Baybo? You're my one and only.

I am her one and only. I can't get kidnapped. I can't disappear. I have to be a good little girl. I am my mother's only one.

So I turn around. I run by the white car again, but then I slow down. The corner's in sight. Once I get there, I'm almost home.

The wind has stopped, and it's quiet now. I strain to hear "Jingle Bells" or "Santa Claus Is Coming to Town." But I don't hear any songs. All I hear is my mother's voice, calling me home.

• • • •

I am five now, and I am having a birthday party. I have my own cake, and my father has his own cake, too; we are having our birthday parties together this year. Little Nana is at our party with Big Nana, Aunt Lorraine, Uncle Jimmy and Uncle Leroy, but no children because I don't know the children who live on our street, only the boy downstairs. He's the landlord's son, and I don't like him because the landlord said no dogs allowed.

Mama lights the candles on my cake. There are seven: five for my birthday, one for luck and one to grow on. I squeeze my eyes tight, wish for Buttons to come home, take a deep breath and blow out my candles. My father's cake has so many candles that you could roast marshmallows over it. "How many candles do you have?" I ask. He says, "Too many," then he blows them out. I don't ask him to wish for Buttons to come back because I know he's saving his wishes for the baby that Mama wants. I imagine that my mother and father will go for a ride someday after my father's big wish and that they'll find a river and sit beside it until a baby comes floating by. I hope it's a girl baby. I think, wouldn't it be perfect if both our birthday wishes came true and Mama got her baby and Buttons came home?

• • • •

"Put Duffy back in his bowl," Mama says. She's cooking supper, and I'm in the kitchen sitting on the floor playing with Duffy and watching her. I put him back in his bowl.

"Wash your hands," Mama says.

I walk into the bathroom and run cold water over my fingers. Sometimes we eat supper in the afternoon, and sometimes we eat after dark. My father works crazy hours, Mama says. That's why we eat at different times. Today, we are eating early. I put the knives and forks on the table. My father is putting on his uniform. He comes to the table in his navy blue police jacket with the big gold buttons. He is handsome in his uniform. My mother thinks so, too. She tells him all the time that he looks like Sergeant Preston.

"Who is Sergeant Preston?" I ask.

"Someone on the radio," Mama tells me.

"How do you know what someone on the radio looks like?"

"I imagine what he looks like, and I imagine he looks just like your father."

After dinner, my father goes to work. I take Duffy out of his bowl while Mama cleans up. I am careful to hold on to him so that Mama doesn't step on him by accident. I poke his face and his feet, poke, poke, and Mama says, "Stop tormenting that poor creature." So I put him on the floor for just a minute so I'm not tempted to torment him anymore. There he is right in front of me, and Mama backs up. She's not looking so she doesn't see, and she steps on him. There's a big, awful, loud, terrible crunch.

I pick up Duffy. He can't hide his head, it's got nowhere to go. His shell is cracked, and his insides are on the outside. But his tiny eyes are still open and blinking. He looks almost the same, just a little confused.

"Do you think he'll be all right, Mama?"

"I don't know. Let me see him."

Mama is more upset than I am. "I think I killed him," she says.

But the next morning, though Duffy's shell is broken and he still looks confused, he is alive.

Wanted — Dead or Alive

I have a friend! Her name is Mary Toomey, and she lives across the street and down the street. And you know what? Her mother lets her go to the store all by herself! Mama says Mary Toomey is far too little to be able to walk anywhere by herself, let alone to the store, which is on the corner of a busy street where bad men ride up and down waiting to kidnap pretty little girls. I worry about Mary Toomey and the bad men, but I'm glad that her mother lets her walk to the store anyway, or we wouldn't be friends, because that's how we met.

I'm getting to be a big girl now, so Mama lets me cross our street. But she won't let me play in the street, even though everyone else can. I don't care.

I like going to the store. She sends me to buy cigarettes or ice cream or bread or milk. Every day I ask, "Mama, do you want me to go to the store now?" Some days she says yes — and gives me a penny for going — and some days she says no.

I always buy mint juleps with my penny, which I share with Mary Toomey. Mary Toomey shares her licorice with me. She likes root beer barrels the best because they last the longest, but you can't share those. Mama says, "I don't want you eating root beer barrels because they're dangerous. You could choke on them."

Mary Toomey and I play house most afternoons. We dress in our mothers' old clothes, and we dress our babies in their clothes. Then we put them in their carriages and walk them up and down Calvin Street because fresh air is good for them. Kevin Cunningham sits on the cement steps, pops caps with a rock and calls us babies and idiots, but we ignore him. Mama says that's the way to deal with people who tease. Ignore them, and they'll go away.

But Kevin Cunningham doesn't go away. He lives in the downstairs of my house, not the way downstairs where the coal is, where the fire burns and where I go sometimes with my father, but downstairs in rooms just like ours. I imagine they're rooms just like ours, but I've never been inside. Kevin Cunningham's parents are mean. And he's mean, too, sitting on his front steps making faces at us. I imagine his rooms are dark and have bolts on all the doors.

I don't really believe that my doll is alive, but I take good care of her just in case. I change her diaper, sing her lullabies and put real milk in her bottle. And I always make her wear a hat when she goes outside. On hot days Mary Toomey and I leave our babies indoors because we don't have nets for their carriages and the mosquitoes are everywhere. "Don't scratch your mosquito bites," Mama says. But I scratch anyway because I am so sweet that the mosquitoes bite me all over, and I am so itchy that I can't help but scratch.

Kevin Cunningham looks at my mosquito bites and pretends to throw up. They are ugly. I have them all over my arms and legs, big red blotches made redder by my picking at them.

"Beverly has cooties. Beverly has cooties," Kevin Cunningham sings.

Mary Toomey doesn't have even one cootie because she doesn't scratch her mosquito bites, but that doesn't get in the way of Kevin's songs. "Mary has cooties. Mary has cooties," he continues.

I pick up a rock and throw it at him to make him stop singing. It's just a small rock, a pebble really, no bigger than a rubber ball you play jacks with. But it hits him on the head, and he goes wailing to his mother. She charges out of the house with a spatula in her hand. I think she is going to beat me with it so I start screaming, and my mother comes running. She yells at Mrs. Cunningham, who yells back at her, and before I know it Mary Toomey has been sent home, and I have been sent to my room.

Again.

My room isn't a bad place to be. It has elephants and circus tents and clowns on the wallpaper. And I have my very own wind-up Ferris wheel, which sings a happy song, plus my dolls to keep me company. After a while Mama calls me out of my room for a snack, a grilled cheese sandwich, my favorite. Then she sends me to the store for ice cream. Kevin Cunningham is on the sidewalk riding MY bike. I threaten him. "You better get off my bike right now, or I'll tell my father."

"Make me," he says.

"GET OFF MY BIKE NOW!" I yell.

He sticks out his tongue and makes a thhhhhhhhhh sound; then he pedals away. Now he's the one who looks like an idiot because he's way too big for my three-wheeler. He must be eight or nine. But he doesn't care. He pedals as fast as he can, all the way down the street. I don't chase him because I'm going in the opposite direction and because Mama says if you ignore people who tease you, they'll go away.

This time she's right. I watch him until I can't see him anymore. Then I cross the street, stop at Mary Toomey's and yell, "Hi-O Mary! Are you coming out to play?" She skips down the steps, and we go to the store together. I split my mint juleps with her and then we walk back to my house, where Mama gives us some ice cream. Kevin Cunningham has still not returned.

I see him the next day, back on the porch setting off caps. "Where's my bicycle?" I ask.

"I threw it down the sewer," he says.

I am only five, but I know that a bicycle can't fit down a sewer, and I tell him this.

"I chopped it up first, stupid. I chopped it into tiny pieces."

"Mama! Mama! Kevin Cunningham chopped up my bicycle and threw it down the sewer," I holler as I race up the stairs.

Mama says, "I'm sure he didn't do that, Beverly. No one would do that."

"Yes, he did, Mama. He said he did."

I drag Mama downstairs, and Mama says to Kevin Cunningham, "Did you take Beverly's bicycle?"

And he says, "Her bike? That old thing? That's a baby's bike. Why would I take that when I have my own two-wheeler?"

"Tell the truth, Kevin, or God will punish you," I say. "He took it, Mama. He said he took it."

"Did you take it?" she asks him again.

"No. I didn't touch it."

"Yes, you did, you liar." I want to pick up a rock and hit him again, this time right between the eyes. But Mama's there, so I just stick out my tongue.

"If I find out you're lying to me you're going to be in big, big trouble, young man," my mother says to him. Then we go back upstairs.

"Wait till you father comes home. He'll know what to do," Mama says.

My father comes home. He talks to Kevin, who lies again, this time to a policeman in a uniform with a badge and a gun. But Kevin doesn't look like he's lying. He's crossing his heart and hoping to die, and his eyes are getting watery, and he's being so polite. Mrs. Cunningham comes out of the house, sees her son all teary and trembly and starts yelling again, this time at my father.

"Are you sure about this, Beverly?" he turns and asks.

"Yes, Dad. I'm sure. He told me he stuffed my bicycle down the sewer. That's what he said."

"Did you say that, Kevin?"

"I said it, but I didn't mean it. Everyone knows a bicycle can't fit down a sewer."

But the bicycle is gone. I go to bed and get up the next morning, and it's still gone. And when I see Kevin Cunningham walking down the street, he smiles a pretend smile, and then he laughs at me.

I've Got a Secret

I am in big, big trouble. Mama told me, "Beverly, if I come out here one more time and those clothespins aren't in the basket where they belong, you're going to be in big trouble. Do you understand?"

I understood. I crossed my heart and hoped to die and swore on Duffy's life that I wasn't going to throw clothespins across to the neighbor's porch ever, ever again. The clothespins never reach the porch anyway. They land on the cement next to our house, and most break when they fall, the little metal parts snapping off. But I always collect the ones that aren't broken and put them back in the basket.

We live up almost on the very top of our house, and there's an identical house next to us with a back porch just like ours. There's a lady who lives there who hangs her laundry on a line just like ours, too. She's pretty, almost as pretty as Mama, and she's almost as nice. She waves at me, smiles, says "Hi, Beverly" and asks what am I doing today. I never throw clothespins when she's there. I wouldn't want to hit her. But I throw them when she isn't there, and I throw them when I shouldn't. I throw them even after swearing on Duffy's life and promising Mama that I won't.

It is a hot day, too hot to play with Mary Toomey, too hot to go to the store, even. Mama has the fan on in the kitchen, but it doesn't help. The air is heavy and still. There is some shade on the porch, so I go out there, but it doesn't help. I am so hot that I am shiny like furniture just polished. I am so hot that I have to keep moving or I'll stick like gum. I am so hot that I don't know what I should do.

I reach into the clothespin basket, and I think that I'll throw one. Just one. That's all. Then I'll stop. One doesn't count. One won't be missed. One isn't really breaking a promise. God wouldn't care about one.

But I guess I throw more than one, because when I start the basket is full of brand new clothespins that my mother just bought at the A&P, and when I stop I look into the basket and it's empty. I know that I am in big, big trouble.

Mama is in the kitchen in front of the fan sipping ice water and waiting for the washing machine to stop. It chugs and shudders. I think it's on spin dry.

If I race down to the yard right now, right this second, and collect all the clothespins and put them back — even though they were brand new and now they're not — maybe she won't notice. Maybe she'll forget that she just bought them. But it is so, so hot, fire hot, hot like the red coals that my father shovels into the furnace, that I don't want to race anywhere. I don't want to move. Mama isn't moving. I'll pick up the clothespins in a while. I'll sit a little first. I'll pick up the clothespins later.

So I walk into the kitchen, plant myself on a chair and wait for the fan to cool me. I love our fan. It nods back and forth, back and forth, and you don't have to do anything but sit and wait for it to blow on you.

Mama says, "Well, look at the time. I better start dinner." So I get up, too, and get Duffy out of his dish to give him some cool air. But his water is hot, so I ask Mama, "Can I change it?" She says, "Yes, but don't put Duffy on the floor. I don't want to step on him again."

I put him on the floor anyway. It's funny how he really doesn't seem to mind not having a shell anymore. He used to look embarrassed. Now he looks resigned. That's what Mama says.

"What does resigned mean?" I asked her.

"It means when you accept a bad situation. When it doesn't make you mad or sad anymore."

I am resigned to Kevin Cunningham living downstairs, but I am not resigned to having to talk to him.

Duffy waddles off across the floor, heading for under the refrigerator, which is his favorite place. At the very same time, Mama, who is standing at the stove and facing it, steps back and steps on Duffy. I drop his dish full of water all over the floor and holler, "Look out, Mama!" because in the second before it happens, I can see it coming. I can see her blue sneaker about to make contact. But it's too late. I hear a soft squish, and then I hear Mama scream.

We make a coffin out of my Cinderella watch box and bury Duffy in the dirt behind our house. I cry because I know why Duffy died. I killed him. Not only did I not listen to Mama, I also swore on Duffy's life that I would never, ever throw clothespins again and then I did and broke my promise to God. I don't tell Mama this. She thinks it's all her fault. I want to say it isn't. It's mine. I want to confess. But more than anything else I want to pick up the clothespins and put them back in Mama's basket, do what Mama said and not put Duffy on the floor, and walk into the kitchen and find him where he belongs — on the counter in his dish.

Mama doesn't notice the clothespins all over one side of the yard. If we'd buried Duffy there she would have walked right on them. Then she'd have known why Duffy died.

But I can change things. I can make everything right. I can undo all that's been done. I know I can.

After we bury Duffy, we walk back upstairs. Mama goes into the bathroom to wash her face and hands. I yell, "I forgot something," and hurry back down the steps out to the yard and fill my pockets with Mama's new clothespins. Oh, what a mess they are, all broken and dirty. I collect them anyway, then run — who cares about the heat now — back up the stairs and out to our porch.

I return the clothespins to the basket, run back into the kitchen and look in Duffy's dish, certain that I've made everything right and that we can go back to the way things were.

But Duffy isn't there. Duffy is still in the dirt in the back yard. Duffy is still dead.

Maybe, it takes time. Maybe, if I go into my room and

pray. Maybe, if I am very, very quiet and very, very still, it will happen.

I lie on my bed and wait. I wait for it to get cooler and darker. I wait for my father to come home. I wait for a good fairy or God to make things right.

But Duffy stays dead, and no matter what anyone says, I know that Duffy is dead because of me.

Ding Dong School

*L*orraine buys me a red pencil case that has a see-through ruler, a pencil, two crayons and a compass inside. Big Nana gives me a dollar and says, "This is for luck." Little Nana tells me a story about a boy who didn't want to go to school, who cried himself to sleep every night for weeks because he didn't want to leave his mother or his friends, but who, on the very first day, liked school so much that he cried when it was time to go home.

I am getting to be a big girl, now — so big that I will be starting school in a few weeks. Mama takes me to a store in Boston where a lady measures me for a uniform. All the children wear uniforms at this school, Mama says. All the girls wear navy blue shoes with thick straps, not ties, so my mother buys me these, too.

The uniform arrives in the mail a few weeks later: a navy blue jumper and two white blouses. Mama calls to me, "It's here, Beverly. Come try it on." I am in my room playing records. "Watch out. Listen to what I have to say. I'll give you some good advice, some good advice today. Watch out. Listen, you little girls and boys. Stay away from knives and swords, they are not children's toys."

I slip off my shirt and shorts and put on my uniform. Mama gets sad. "Is it ugly? Don't you like it?"

"I like it. It's just that my baby's growing up," she says, hugging me.

There was supposed to be a real baby. I know because I heard Mama talking to Big Nana and Big Nana warning Mama, "Don't count your chickens before they're hatched." I don't understand what chickens have to do with babies or how you can count something before it's born. But Mama went away again, and I was certain that this time she'd come home with a brother or a sister for me. But she didn't. She came home with a doll instead, a grown-up doll, with long blonde hair, eyes that open and close, long legs and real patent leather shoes.

"You have to be careful you don't drop it," Mama said.

"I'm sorry it's just a doll."

I was sorry, too, though not because it was a doll but because Mama was sad. I loved the doll. I named her Mary because her hair is like Mary Toomey's, full of pretty, soft curls.

"Can I take Mary to school, Mama?"

Mama says, "No. Mary has to stay home. Dolls aren't allowed at school."

"Can I take Mary Toomey to school?"

"Maybe some day," Mama says. "If Sister says."

Sister is Sister Patricia Ann. I am five-and-a-half, and I am not afraid of her, though Mary Toomey said she would be afraid. She thinks nuns are scary, but I don't. Mama always says, "Good morning, Sisters" when we're walking home from Mass, even when she doesn't know the sisters' names. And they always say "Good morning" to her and to me.

Mama says that sisters are very special people who are married to God and who don't have children of their own, so they love other people's children instead. "You have to try to be very good for Sister, because if you're not, God will be sad," Mama says.

When I say my prayers at night, I pray for Sister, too. God bless Mama and Dad and Aunt Lorraine and Big Nana and Little Nana and Buttons and Sister, too.

On the first day of first grade Mama walks me to school. We get to the schoolyard, and it is crowded with boys and girls I don't know. Mama doesn't know anyone either. A mean-looking nun rings a very big bell, and the boys make one line and the girls make another. I kiss Mama goodbye and follow the crowd.

I sit in the front seat of the third row. There are seventy children in my class. Sister counts them. Sister Patricia Ann is pretty, even without hair and lipstick. She has smooth skin and nice teeth, and I like her. She stands in the front of the room and says, "Good morning, boys and girls." And we stand and say, "Good morning, Sister."

Then we say a "Hail Mary," an "Our Father" and a "Glory be to God." Then we say the "Pledge of Allegiance."

I know all my prayers. I know who made me. God made me. God made everyone. God made heaven and earth, too.

"Very good," Sister says.

"Sister, Sister!" I wave my hand. I want to say more. I want to say WHY God made me, but Sister says, "Not now, Beverly. Let someone else have a turn."

I don't know any of the children in my room, but I talk to them anyway. I talk to the girl behind me and to the girl next to me, and Sister says, "There will be no talking when I'm talking. Do you understand?"

The first day of first grade is very long. I watch the clock in the front of the room, I look at my Cinderella watch and I try to pay attention to Sister. But I am think-ing about my mother and Mary Toomey and what they are doing at home and whether Mama misses me. At ten o'clock we go outdoors for recess. The boys play in one half of the yard; the girls in the other. I think about run-ning home, but I'm not sure of the way.

At noon, Mama comes to school to walk me home for lunch. She asks me how my morning was. I say it was fun, though I'm not sure it was. I'm not sure I want to go back to school ever again.

Mama makes tomato soup with milk for lunch. Some-times she makes it with water, but today is special, so she makes it with milk the way I like it. We have cookies, too — Oreos. Mary Toomey knocks on the door. "Was school fun?" I say it was. Then Mary goes home, and Mama walks me back to school.

I walk by myself the next day, and the next: to school, home for lunch, back to school, home again. I like the walk. It's the best part of the day. I make up stories in my head. I sing songs.

In school I make up stories and sing songs when I'm not supposed to. They just slip out. I don't mean to talk when Sister's talking. I don't mean to interrupt.

Sister puts Scotch tape on my lips. Some of the kids laugh, but Sister scolds them and threatens to put Scotch tape on their lips. When lunch time comes, Sister says I can remove the tape.

I walk home. Mama says, "You're very quiet today. Is everything all right?"

I say, "I don't like school, Mama. I miss you."

"I miss you, too. But you have to go to school. That's part of growing up."

I don't want to grow up. I want to stay home with my mother, listen to records, help her set the table and walk to the store with Mary Toomey.

Mama says, "Give it time, Baybo. You'll get used to it. Once you start reading and writing you'll like it so much that you won't want to come home."

But I know that's never going to happen. Even if I do like school someday I'll always like home better because that's where Mama is.

Mary Toomey (far right) and me (second from right)

Truth or Consequences

Mama has been looking at the ducks for a long time. We sit at the counter at Woolworth's, and there they are in the mirror: a mother and her three babies. They're lawn decorations, Mama has explained. Just ceramic, but they look so real, don't they?

We don't have a lawn. All we have is the wooden porch where the laundry hangs to dry. But Mama has been saving up for the ducks, putting spare change in a jar over the stove, because she wants them for our house in the country. She has already bought the big green chair and the shiny coffee table with a glass top that sit in the living room and that I'm not allowed to touch. No one lives in this room, so why does she call it a living room, I wonder? The door is always closed, and in the winter when you open it, it's so cold that you can see your breath.

When it's not cold, my father and I watch TV in this room. He sits on the green chair, though Mama doesn't want him to. He says, "Why not, Dorothy? Why should I sit on a hard chair when we have this one?" So Mama says, "OK," though you can tell that it isn't OK at all. She puts a white sheet over the coffee table and moves it as far away from the chair as possible. Then she says we are definitely not allowed to use that, ever. It won't be special if we do.

My father says, "Dot, we don't have a house in the country." But my mother says, "We will, Larry, and it's important that when we get there we have a few nice pieces of furniture."

The ducks aren't furniture. You can't sit on them or lay things on them. "I know I don't need them," Mama says, staring into the mirror, gazing at their reflection. "But I can picture them marching across the lawn. I just have to have them."

I can picture them, too. I dream along with Mama, imagining a house with a screen door, big lawn, and trees outside my window and no Kevin Cunningham downstairs. "When we get our house in the country, will I go to a different school?"

"Yes," Mama says.

"What school?"

"I don't know."

"I like my school."

"I know you do."

"Will Mary Toomey move to a house in the country, too?"

"I don't know, Beverly. Probably not. But you'll make other friends."

Mama puts out her cigarette. I slurp on my soda, and she says, "Don't do that. It's rude. You should never make noise when you eat. It's important to have good table manners. It's polite."

We walk over to where the ducks are and look at them up close. This is what we always do. The ducks are heavy and have long orange beaks, orange feet and black eyes. The mother is three times the size of the babies, the babies are all a little different. I like the mother best. I like her because she looks as if she knows where she's going. Mama says she likes the babies best because they look as if they're perfectly content just to follow.

We don't buy flowers on our way home anymore because Mama is saving her flower money, too, and her cigarette money sometimes, though this is hard, she says. But the flower man sees us walking by and yells, "What? No flowers today, Mrs. Curtin?" And Mama shakes her head no and explains that she won't be buying any flowers for a while. The flower man says, "Wait just a minute," ducks back into his shop and returns with two red carnations. "One for you, and one for you," he says, handing them to us. "Beautiful flowers were meant for beautiful ladies."

"Thank you," I say, even before Mama can say thank you. And I smile at her, and she smiles back because this time she didn't have to remind me about being polite.

• • • •

On weekends, Mary Toomey and I play school and I am Sister Patricia Ann, and she is me, and I teach her how to spell cat, dog and cow. And I teach her the acts of faith, hope and love.

I pick stars off my papers and glue them on hers. I give her 100 percent, even if she makes her D's backwards. Only once do I tape her mouth closed.

Mary Toomey is so smart, smarter than some of the kids in my class. "Why can't she go to school with me?" I ask Mama.

"Because she isn't old enough," Mama says.

"But she knows her letters and her numbers and her prayers. It's not fair that she can't go to school."

"That's up to Sister," Mama says. "It's not up to me."

"Mary Toomey is my very best friend," I tell Sister. "She lives on my street. She's a good little girl who is very pretty and can count and spell and knows all her prayers."

"That's very interesting, Beverly."

"And she wants to go to school so she can learn more."

"That's commendable that she wants to learn more."

"Do you think she should go to school, Sister?"

"Of course, I do. All children should go to school."

"Really?"

"Yes, Beverly. School is very important."

I run home at lunch time to tell Mama that Sister said Mary Toomey could come to school. "She said 'Yes,' Mama. She said I could take her."

"Are you sure about this, Beverly. Sister has enough children in her class. Are you sure she wants another?"

"Yes, Mama. I'm sure."

I race across the street. "Mary, Mary. Guess what? Sister said you could come to school with me."

"I can? Are you sure?"

"I'm sure. I'm positive."

All weekend I prepare her for the big day. We add. We spell. We kneel. We stand. We bless ourselves. We pray. On Monday morning, Mary is at my door in a red plaid dress with a red bow in her hair. Her mother is behind her, wearing her Sunday coat and hat.

Mrs. Toomey insists upon walking Mary to school. She explains to Mary, "Remember you're just visiting, dear. You're just going to school for this day only." But I say, "No, no, no. Sister said she could come to school every day." Mama and Mrs. Toomey think that I have misunderstood, but I know I didn't. I can't wait for Sister to meet Mary. I can't wait for Mary to meet Sister. I'll find a folding chair and put it beside my desk. I'll hold Mary's hand when we walk home for lunch. We can practice our spelling as we walk. I am so excited that I want to run all the way to school, but Mrs. Toomey is like Duffy use to be, very slow, so it takes us a long time to get there.

Sister is outside in the schoolyard. She's ringing the big bell. "Sister, Sister! This is my friend Mary Toomey. This is the girl I told you about." Sister looks puzzled.

"She's come to school with me just like you said."

Sister frowns.

"It's very nice to meet you, Sister," Mrs. Toomey says, smiling.

Sister isn't smiling. Sister is staring at me.

"What do you mean she's come to school, Beverly."

"You said she could come, Sister. Remember?"

"I never said any such thing."

"Yes, you did, Sister. On Friday, when we talked."

"You're correcting me, Beverly?"

"No, Sister. I'm not correcting you. But you said..."

"What I said was that all children should go to school. I never said anything about this child going to this school. What exactly are you trying to pull?"

Trying to pull? I don't know what this means. I'm not pulling anything. Mama said not to pull on her coat, and I don't, not all the time.

I look at Mary Toomey, and her pretty blue eyes are filling with tears. I look at Mrs. Toomey, and her face is getting red. I look at Sister, and she is angry, angrier than I've ever seen her. Now they are all looking at me, and I am so confused that I don't know what to do. Sister said Mary could come, and Mary is smart, and the school day is long, and I miss Mary so much. It's hard sitting still in one chair in a room crowded with boys and girls you don't even know, and I know Mary. I thought if she came to school, the walks to and from wouldn't be so lonely, and the day wouldn't be so long. Maybe Sister didn't say she could come, exactly, but she said she *should* come. And, oh, I'm sorry, Mrs. Toomey, that you bought Mary that pretty dress. I'm sorry you got all dressed up and walked here in your shoes that hurt. And I'm sorry you have to walk home now.

"Oh, Mary, don't cry. I'm sorry. I'm sorry. No, Sister, no. I don't want you to call my mother. I will stop these tears. I will. I promise."

Sister rings the bell, and Mary and her mother walk out of the playground and down the street. All the children in uniforms line up, boys on one side of the playground, girls on the other, and everyone single-files into the building. Sister follows with me in tow. "I don't want you ever, ever pulling anything like this again. Do you understand, Beverly? Look at the confusion you caused. Look at what you've done. Do you know why this happened? It happened because you heard what you wanted to hear. Because you didn't listen. Because you wanted your own way. And you got it. Are you happy now?"

• • • •

I am so unhappy. This is the worst day of my life. I don't want to go back to school, Mama. All the kids laughed. Sister hates me. I hate me.

Mama puts on a pretty dress and says, "Don't leave the house, and don't touch the stove," She walks to school and apologizes to Sister. She simply didn't understand, Mama says.

"She needs to listen better," Sister insists.

"She will," Mama tells her.

Over cocoa made with milk and sweetened with sugar, Mama tells me she's talked with Mrs. Toomey and straightened out everything.

"Mrs. Toomey isn't mad anymore? I can go over there right now if I want?"

Yes, Mama says. Now I'm sobbing, great hiccuping cries, worse than when I killed Duffy. I'm sobbing because Mrs. Toomey isn't mad at me anymore and Sister won't be mad tomorrow, because Mama went and made everything right.

"I know how much you wanted Mary to go to school with you, Beverly," Mama says. "You wanted it so much I'm certain you believe Sister said she could come. You didn't hear the real words Sister said because you had your own words running around in your head. Maybe you should have listened better, but I know you didn't mean any harm."

I decide not to go to Mary Toomey's. I stay home with Mama, dry my eyes, sit at the kitchen table and snap peas while she peels potatoes for French fries. We sing as we work. We sing my new favorite song, "Rap, tap, tap, rap, tap, tap, bumpety boo. That's how the old cobbler mends every shoe." We're singing so loud that we don't hear my father climbing the steps. All of a sudden we look, and he's standing at the kitchen door, filling the whole doorway, and he's singing, too, "Rap, tap, tap, rap tap, tap, bumpety boo." And I think this wasn't the worst day of my life after all.

Name That Tune

"*S*shhh," my father says at noon when I come home from school.

"Why is Mama sleeping? Why isn't she making our lunch?"

"She's tired, sweetheart. How would you like some fried bologna?"

I love it when my father makes fried bologna. He cooks it so that it's crisp all over. He slathers the bread with mustard, adds a piece of yellow cheese, puts the hot bologna on top and slices it in half. I eat it greedily, while it's warm, crust and all.

"Your mother is going to be lying down a lot for a while, and what I need from you is your promise that you won't make any noise when she's resting. It's very important that she gets her sleep. Do you think you can make your own lunch the days I'm not home and that you can very quietly let yourself in the house in the afternoon after school?"

"Is Mama sick, Dad?"

"No, she's not sick. She's just tired and needs to stay off her feet for a few weeks. She needs to rest more."

Mama is still resting when I get home in the afternoon. I don't run up the stairs and shout "Hey, Mama, I'm home." I walk up the two flights on the tips of my toes, and I gently open the door. My father has gone to work. Sometimes he works days, and sometimes he works nights. When he works nights and sleeps days I am very quiet, just as I am now. I sit on my bed in my room and read "Cinderella" and "Snow White" and "Nurse Nancy," which is my favorite book. Nurse Nancy lives in a house in the country. She's an only child, like me, but she's a nurse. When her friends' babies get sick and a leg falls off or a younger brother colors a face with crayon, Nurse Nancy knows how to get the face clean again and how to mend the broken leg. She wears a white dress, like the kind Big Nana wears, but over it she wears a red striped apron. Plus, pinned on her head is a crisp white nurse's hat.

I want a nurse's hat for Christmas and a nurse's kit, too, full of pills and Band-Aids, and my very own "Nurse Beverly" badge. Nurse Nancy has a baby carriage, a real carriage that real babies could ride in if they were small enough. She pushes the carriage all over her neighborhood, collecting sick babies, and wheels them back to her house, where she fixes them in her very own hospital room.

Nurse Nancy lives on a tree-lined street where all the children live in houses with yards. I don't have a house with a yard, but there are a few trees on our street, and I am making my bedroom into a hospital room just like Nurse Nancy's. I already have a bed for sick babies and a bassinet where sick babies can be bathed. When Santa gets me my hat and my badge, I plan to collect all the sick babies on my street and make them better, just like Nurse Nancy does. I would like to ask Santa for a new doll carriage, too, because mine is small and old, but I'm already asking him for the hat, the badge, the pills and a baby sister or brother. I don't want to ask for so much that he forgets the real baby, which is the most important gift. I'm getting that for Mama.

I hear Mama now in the hall walking toward me. My door opens.

"Hi, Baybo," she says. "What are you doing?"

"Playing Nurse Nancy."

"Are you hungry?"

"A little."

"Want some chicken noodle soup?"

"Sure."

Mama is in the kitchen making the soup. Should she be? My father said she needs to stay off her feet.

Mama laughs when I tell her this. "I can't stay off my feet all day and all night now, can I? I have to eat too, you know. Don't worry. I've had plenty of rest today. You were a good girl, letting me sleep like that."

My father brings home a man I don't know, a friend from work, a big man with a big smile. My father has two jobs now because my mother needs to stay off her feet and can't work at Howard Johnson's anymore.

My father likes his second job. He's learning how to fix radios and TVs. On the kitchen shelf, where my mother used to keep jelly glasses, he has pieces of radios — speakers, tubes and wires — that he plays with until there are voices and notes coming out of the speakers.

Mama says, "Larry, you can fix anything." Then she smiles at him. Mama is beautiful when she smiles. Her eyes lose their sadness.

The man I don't know has brought a big suitcase, which he lays on the kitchen table.

"Well, hello there, Blondie," he says to me. "Where'd you get all those curls?"

I say, "From my father," because that's where Mama says I got them, and the man laughs.

"Do you like to sing, Blondie?"

I nod.

"I know *you* like to sing," he says to Mama. She looks at my father.

The man opens the suitcase; inside are knobs, buttons, a microphone and something that looks like a record.

"It is a record," he explains. "Only there's nothing on it. But this here machine, this baby, lets you put your own voice on a record. Want to see how it works?"

The man plugs one wire into the wall and another into something else and says, "Testing one, two, three." He hands Mama the mike and says, "Sing." And then he says, "No, no, wait. Do you have a record you can sing with?"

Mama puts the record "Down Yonder" on the Victrola, and sings into the mike, and my father sings along with her. They say, "Beverly, you sing, too," and I do. Everyone is laughing, and Mama's eyes are shining. When the song is over the man says, "Keep going. Keep going." So Mama tells me to recite a poem and I recite my favorite poem. Then she says, "Sing a song," so I sing "Because of You."

Now it's Mama's turn, and my father says, "No fooling around now, Dot. This is forever."

Mama puts a different record on the Victrola and sings along with it: "Maybe I'm right and maybe I'm wrong, maybe I'm weak and maybe I'm strong, but nevertheless I'm in love with you." She sings the whole song in a voice like you'd hear on the radio. Then she sings, "I have mixed emotions when it comes to loving you." Mama's voice is so sweet and beautiful that the man with the big smile gets tears in his eyes.

Mama and I sing "Slowpoke" together. Then my father recites a poem that I don't understand and my mother says, "Oh, Larry, you can't say that. This is being recorded." And she laughs, and my father laughs, and the big man laughs, too.

• • • •

I am a good girl. I help Mama set the table, I dry the dishes and I am quiet and good for a long, long time. My father tells me every day that I am such a big help and such a good girl. I sit in my room and read my "Nurse Nancy" book, or I play my records or practice my letters — Sister says I need to practice because my letters are sloppy. I don't leave my bedroom door open so I can listen to Mama and Dad when they talk. I try to be good. I try to be like Baby Jesus. In school we're learning about Baby Jesus. Baby Jesus is the true meaning of Christmas, Sister says, not Santa Claus and certainly not presents. Baby Jesus is all that's important.

I wonder if Baby Jesus had to stay in his room while his mother slept in the room next to his. I wonder what he did while all the adults talked. He didn't have a record player because record players weren't invented yet, and he didn't have books like "Nurse Nancy," either. I wonder if he had a friend like Mary Toomey.

• • • •

One afternoon I come home from Mary Toomey's, and Mama is all dressed up in shoes and nylons with seams; her hair is curled, and she looks as if she is going to a party.

"We're going to go to Simeone's to celebrate," my father says.

"Celebrate what, Dad?"

They look at each other and smile. My father says, "We're celebrating that your mother is feeling better and doesn't have to stay off her feet anymore. Dr. McSweeney said she can go out and even go dancing now if she wants."

But Mama doesn't want to go dancing. She wants to go to Simeone's, a restaurant that has red-checked table-cloths, candles on the tables and waiters who talk funny.

My father says, "Why don't you get spaghetti, Beverly, or ravioli?" But I say, "No. I want grilled cheese," because that's what I always have. And when he argues that I should really try something different, that I can't live on grilled cheese forever, Mama says, "Let her get what she wants, Larry."

My mother looks pretty tonight. Her cheeks are pink, her eyes are bright, and she looks like she looks when she's singing.

And that's what it feels like for days and days — like Mama is singing inside her head where we can't hear. I get up in the morning, and she's at the stove in her night-gown, but she seems dressed up somehow. It's like there's a party going on in another room that only she knows about.

Mama and Little Nana

As the World Turns

*M*ama takes me to see Santa Claus. We go by train to Boston to Jordan Marsh because that's where the real Santa is. I wear a plaid wool coat with a matching wool hat that itches, but I don't complain. We're going to see Santa Claus!

I have my list in my hand in my mitten. I printed it over and over so that it's neat and all the words are spelled right. We take an escalator up, up, up, and when we get off we are in a different world.

There are trains chugging and hooting on tables, shelves full of beautiful dolls with eyes that open and close and so many games. There are stuffed animals, barking dogs, meowing cats and a monkey playing a drum. There's a clown, a real clown, juggling and another one blowing up balloons and turning them into animals. And a clown makes me a dog; and it's pink and doesn't look like a dog at all, but I say "Thank you" and clutch it tight because I love my balloon dog.

There is a long line of children and no Santa Claus in sight, but Mama says Santa is there at the end of the line. So we wait. It's hot. I unbutton my coat and Mama holds my hat. It gets hotter just standing there, so we take off our coats and hold those, too.

But the line moves. Mama talks to a lady in front of us, the clowns come around and do tricks, and time passes.

Now it's my turn, and here I am walking up to Santa, climbing on his lap and smiling for a picture. He smiles, too; then he turns and says, "What do you want Santa to bring you?" I open my list. I can see that the paper is wrinkled and that some of the words are smudged. So I tell him that I want a nurse's kit, a hat and a badge. But the most important thing, I say, is a baby for Mama — a girl or a boy, we don't care. Santa looks at Mama, and she smiles; and he smiles and I know he's going to bring a baby. I'm sure he will because he's Santa Claus. I know that Baby Jesus is more important and that Christmas is really all about Baby Jesus, but I'm sitting on Santa's lap, and he's listening to me. He's asking if I've been a good little girl, and I have, and I know this means that I will get everything I want.

So I ask for a new carriage, too. "If there's an extra, Santa. And if you can fit it in your sleigh." He gives me a coloring book, crayons and a red lollipop. I say, "Thank you, Santa." Then it's the next person's turn, and Mama and I walk away. She buys me a surprise present that comes out of a plastic clown's mouth. We go to Arch Street Shrine to say a prayer and light a candle. Then we go to Colestone's and get macaroni and cheese. I open my present, and it's Cinderella cut-outs. I say to Mama, "This has been the best day."

She nods and says, "They don't get much better."

• • • •

Mama buys the ducks for her house in the country. Her money jar is full, finally. She counts out the change, and there's enough. "It'll be my Christmas present from me to me," she says.

On Saturday, after we go to the butcher, the baker and the cobbler, we head for the five-and-ten, straight to where the ducks live. Mama doesn't have a cigarette and coffee at the counter the way she always does, and I don't have a vanilla milk shake, though I want one. I get Cracker Jacks instead because Mama wants to go home and put those ducks in the living room where they belong.

The saleslady wraps each separately. Mama carries the mother and one baby, and I carry the other two. I am very careful not to bang into anything, and when we climb on the bus I keep the ducks close to me.

The living room is freezing when we open the door. Mama unwraps the ducks carefully and places them on the hardwood floor. They look funny there, marching across wood, but Mama says they won't be marching across wood forever. "You wait and see, Beverly. Those ducks are going to be strutting across a lawn sooner than you think."

My father comes home and opens the living room door. "They're great looking ducks, Dot," he yells down the hall.

Mama laughs. "You wait and see, Larry. Those ducks are only there temporarily. They have just begun their journey."

•   •   •   •

My father brings home a Christmas tree. It's a funny looking thing, lopsided, bare in places. My mother shakes her head and says, "That tree is a challenge."

My father gets his tool kit and a saw. A while later he calls for us to come see the tree. Now it looks like a real Christmas tree, even and straight and tall. Now it looks almost grand.

"I told you you could fix anything," my mother says.

"How did you do it, Dad?"

"Magic," he tells me, then shows me how he cut branches from the good side, and drilled holes into the bad side and glued in branches. There are Christmas carols on the radio, eggnog in the refrigerator and mince for pie in the kitchen cabinet. I think, Christmas is really just around the corner now.

•   •   •   •

Something has happened. Mama is crying. I hear her behind her closed bedroom door. Mona comes to visit, but she doesn't sit at the kitchen table and have tea. She goes into Mama's bedroom, and they talk in whispers.

Lorraine comes over and gives me a hug and a Hershey chocolate bar, then disappears into the bedroom, too. My father says, "Go play in your room, Beverly," and I do. I wonder if Baby Jesus had to stay in his room while his mother cried in the room next to his.

Dr. McSweeney comes to our house. He carries his black bag into my mother's room. My father goes to follow, and he says, "No. You wait here."

I sit with my father at the kitchen table. He is so worried that he has forgotten to tell me to go to my room. I try not to make any noise. I try not to breathe. The doctor is in the room for a long time, and when he comes out he doesn't say hello to me the way he usually does. He talks to my father. He says Mama has to go to the hospital. He says it doesn't look good, that it's too soon, that he doesn't know why, that sometimes these things happen.

Mama comes out of the bedroom. She is the color of chalk, her eyes look bruised and she is bent over. I know that I am supposed to be invisible and that I am supposed to say and do nothing, but I run to her and throw my arms around her legs.

"It's OK, Baybo. It's OK," Mama says.

I go to Big Nana's for a few days. She lets me make toast in her funny toaster. She lets me feed the birds. She lets me sit on the stool in the Shamrock Cafe and watch her pour beers, and she introduces me to all her friends.

Lorraine paints my fingernails red and buys me a new Golden book. No one talks about Mama. When I ask what happened, why did the doctor come, and where has Mama gone, everyone says to me, "Ssshh. Don't ask those things."

Santa and me

The Life of Riley

I am in second grade now. Sister Joseph Agnes is my teacher. She is much older and much smaller than Sister Patricia Ann. She is the oldest and smallest sister in the whole, entire school.

You'd think with her being so old and small that she'd have a small voice, too; but her voice is as big and loud as Mr. Cunningham's. When children in her class talk to their neighbors — that's what Sister calls the person you sit next to — she doesn't tape their mouths shut like Sister Patricia Ann does. She hits them on the hand with her pointer, then drags them by their hair to the front of the class.

I try so hard not to talk. I think sometimes that I am going to explode and that words will fly all over the room because I swallow so many. But some I can't swallow. They just pop out of me. Sometimes I whisper to the girl in front of me or the girl beside me or the girl behind me, and whap — there goes the pointer, and my hand stings. Then out pops Sister's hand from a black sleeve, and before I know it I am being dragged hair first to the front of the class, where I have to stand until Sister says, "You may now sit down."

I don't tell my mother that Sister pulls my hair. When she says, "How was school today?" I say, "Fine." And when she says, "How is Sister?" I say, "Fine," too.

• • • •

We get a dog and my father names him Shane. He's small, black and cute and I like him, but I'm not going to love him.

"How come we can have this dog, but we couldn't have Buttons?" I ask my father. "Won't the Cunninghams get mad?"

"It doesn't matter about the Cunninghams," he tells me. "We'll be out of here soon enough."

"Out of here?"

"We're moving," Mama explains.

"Moving? Where are we moving to?"

"It's a surprise," Mama says.

But I don't want to move. I don't want to leave Mary Toomey, the doll hospital in my room or my school, because even though some days I come home with a sore head because Sister pulled my hair, mostly I like school. We're preparing for First Holy Communion, and I know my whole catechism.

Before we make our First Holy Communion in a white dress that looks like a bride's we have to make our first confession. Confession is telling our sins to a priest to obtain forgiveness. You go into a little box at the back of the church, kneel down and tell the priest, who's in the box but invisible, all your sins. Sister says sins are offenses to God. Sister says a sin is when you fight with your brothers and sisters. I don't have brothers and sisters, so I raise my hand. Sister says, "Yes Beverly," and I tell her I don't have any sins because I don't have anyone to fight with. Sister says, "Everyone has sins because we are all flawed human beings, the product of Eden."

When I tell Mama this she says that Sister is wrong, that I am not flawed and that I am too young to have offended God.

•   •   •   •

I wake up on a Saturday morning, and my father and mother say, "Get dressed. We're going for a ride."

It's cold, so I wear leggings; they itch, and the collar of my coat itches under my chin. We ride — my mother and father in the front seat and Shane and I in the back — and I think we're going to look at the peach tree. We're going to see if it's grown. I don't mind the itching or the ride because I can't wait to see that tree. Trees grow fast, faster than people, so I imagine that it's already bigger than I am, maybe even bigger than my father.

I have begged so many times to go back and see our tree, so I know that's the surprise. We ride and ride. I fall asleep. When I wake up we are not in the woods with the lake and the peach tree. We are in a place I've never seen, with no trees and no real houses, only parts of houses, and no roads at all.

"This is it," my father announces. "This is the surprise."

My mother is out of the car and running across the dirt, running like I run when I have a penny in my pocket and I'm on my way to the store, running the way Mary Toomey runs when her mother yells, "Mary. Supper's ready."

This is it, my father says. This is what? I wonder. And then I know. This is the house in the country. This is my mother's house.

I get out of the car, and I'm glad I wore my itchy leggings. The wind stings, and it's freezing; but the sun is warm, and the dirt on the ground is warm and it smells wonderful, like the clothes Mama hangs out to dry. And when I look up I see, not the tops of houses, clouds of smoke or other people's porches, but a big, wide sky.

I don't want to leave Mary Toomey, my room or school. But I like it here outside, where you can see the whole sky, where the ground smells so good that you want to lie down on it, even though it's hard like stone, and where the air is so cold that your teeth hurt.

My father says, "Do you want to see the inside of the house?" We walk on a wide, flat board because there are no steps yet. Inside there are boards for walls, more boards for floors and an upstairs with no walls at all.

"Where will we live?" I say, "Up or down?" And Mama laughs and says, "Up *and* down, Baybo. The whole house is ours."

"The whole house and the whole yard. Are we rich, Mama? Did our ship come in?" And Mama says, "No," and my father laughs. Mama says, "It makes you feel rich, though, doesn't it?"

She says we will grow grass and have a beautiful yard. We will plant flowers and have a garden with our own roses. I think about the flower man, and how he always gives me a flower when I walk by and how I'll miss that.

I think about the five-and-ten, the swirly chairs and vanilla milk shakes, and I wonder where we'll get vanilla milk shakes in the country. I wonder where Mama will buy her dresses, where we'll get our sliced bologna and how Lorraine will ever find us so far from home.

"We'll drive her here," my father says. "We'll drive Big Nana and Little Nana, too. It's not that far. Everyone will visit."

"Mary Toomey, too?"

"If her mother says it's OK."

"Where will I sleep?"

"Anywhere you want."

"Really? Can I sleep upstairs?"

"You sure can. You can even choose which room you want."

The windows aren't in the house yet, just the holes where the windows will be. I look out of all of them. I run from one side of the house to the other, trying to decide which room will be best, trying to imagine my dolls in this place and my hospital.

From every going-to-be window I see parts of houses with no steps and no windows and frozen ground where Mama says there will be lawns. As far as I can see, that's all I see, except for a single tree outside one of the window holes.

It's a skinny tree. It looks like a skinny paintbrush, and I can't imagine it green and full of leaves. But I tell my father that I think I want this room because of the tree. Maybe some birds will make a nest in it, and maybe, if I leave my window open, the birds will fly in and help me make my bed the way they did for Cinderella.

Cinderella didn't have any sisters either, just mean, awful stepsisters who made her work all the time, scrubbing floors and mending their clothes. But she had the birds, the mice and the animals in the forest, and they were even nicer and more helpful than sisters.

I ask my father if there is a forest here, too, and he says

let's take a ride around the block. That's what he calls it, though it isn't a block. A block is square. We drive around in a great, big circle, and I want to ask why he calls it a block when it's a circle. But then I see that in back of some of the houses on the circle there is a forest.

"It's just woods," my father says. "It's not a real forest."

"What's the difference, Dad?"

"Forests are much, much bigger."

But I think this is big. I think this is huge. All those Christmas trees and skinny trees and the smell — like the woods where we planted our peach tree — and the dark, like in storybooks. I'm going to have my own forest.

"What do you think, Baybo?" Mama asks. I think I'm going to miss Mary Toomey, St. Joseph's, the flower man, walking to the store and helping my father shovel coal. I can't imagine the pretty yard that Mama says she can close her eyes and see in her head. I can't imagine not waking up in the room that I always wake up in, and I can't imagine Mama's ducks anywhere but on the living room floor.

But I love the forest, I like the skinny tree, and I think my dolls will like it here. And though Shane isn't Buttons, I like having him in the back seat with me. I like listening to Mama talk about how, come spring, her ducks will be strutting across a brand new lawn, and I'll be sleeping in a brand new room, and we'll all have brand new friends.

Mama is smiling and happy, and I am happy, too.

Shane and me

Mama

Mama is singing, "Oh we ain't got a barrel of money, maybe we're ragged and funny, but we'll travel along, singing a song, side by side." That's her new favorite song. She sings it as she packs.

I hear her on the phone telling Big Nana, "No, I'm not deserting you. No, Ma. I don't think I'm too good for the neighborhood. No, I don't have highfalutin ideas."

I help her wrap plates and cups in old newspapers, and she talks to me about the time she lived in Haverhill. It was the happiest time in her life, she says. "It was the happiest time before I had you."

She was fourteen and lived there for two years. She had her own room, and there was a tree outside her window that looked like lace in the springtime, she says. It was white with the tiniest petals. The house had a big front porch where you could sit and a back yard with a rope swing hanging from a tree. "I met my friend Theresa there. We walked to school together. When I broke my leg, Theresa brought my homework over every afternoon."

Mama says that she broke her leg riding a boy's bicycle she wasn't supposed to be riding, and Big Nana was mad at her for a long time because she couldn't do much around the house with her leg in a cast. But even counting this, it was still the best time in her life, she says. Theresa lived on a big farm, and they had chickens and fresh eggs. Every time my mother would go there, Theresa's mother would send her home with eggs.

"Will we have chickens and fresh eggs at our house in the country?" I ask.

"No, Baybo. But we'll have lots of other things we don't have here." And then she goes off again, planning her garden, her front walk and her rose-covered trellis, which she says is a thing so pretty that I'll have to see it before I can believe it.

Little Nana cries when we say goodbye to her. Her eyes get black, and her nose gets red. My father says, "Mom, we're not moving across the country. It's less than

an hour away. But she hugs me hard and says, "Don't forget me."

• • • •

I don't live on Calvin Street anymore. I live at 47 Davis
Road. There are only three houses on our little road —
one next to us and one across the street. I don't understand why we are number 47 instead of number 3.

Our house is light green and pretty. It has cement front
steps, wooden back steps, windows and walls, but no
lawn, not yet, because it's February and the ground is still
frozen. In the room where I sleep it's cold and I can't see
my tree because the windows are coated with ice.
There's shiny stuff on my walls, like aluminum foil. I
don't have a real ceiling, only boards above my bed.

Sometimes at night when the light from the hall creeps
through the space under and around my door, the shiny
stuff turns into ghosts, and the ghosts are everywhere —
around and above and next to me. They float all over my
room, they grin at me, and when I look toward my window hoping to see the sky, all I see are more ghosts waiting to get in.

"Mama! Mama!" I scream, because if I don't, I know
the ghosts will kidnap me. And Mama comes running,
though she's not supposed to because the floor in my
room is rough, and she tells me, "You'll get splinters if
you go barefoot, so always wear your slippers." But she
comes running barefoot every night when I cry for her.

My father says he's going to finish doing the upstairs
himself. If you do the upstairs yourself, he says, you save
a lot of money. Mama says you would think that with all
it costs for a new house, it would at least come finished.
"Do you want me to sleep up here with you?" she asks.

"No," I say, though that's exactly what I want.

I lie in my new room in my old bed with my eyes
closed so I don't see the ghosts. But I see them anyway
through my closed eyes. I hear them, too, swooshing
around. I try not to breathe. I try to pretend I'm dead so

they won't hurt me, but they know I'm pretending. They come closer and closer until I have to yell for Mama, because only then will they disappear. Mama comes, and the ghosts flee. Mama sits next to me, and I'm not afraid anymore.

I have a new dress for my first day at my new school. I don't have to wear a uniform anymore. I'm going to a public school, not a Catholic school. My teacher will be a person, not a sister.

My mother and father take me to school.

"I don't want you to be scared," my mother says. "You're going to have fun. You're going to meet so many new friends and have so much to do."

I don't think I'm scared, but I know Mama is. She holds my hand as she walks me into school. She squeezes my hand as we stand in the principal's office. The principal is like the mother superior. She's the one in charge. The principal's name is Mrs. Cormey. Mama has told me all this. "We're very glad to have you here, Beverly," Mrs. Cormey says.

Mrs. Cormey walks us down the shiny corridor to Miss Nagel's room. She knocks on the door and opens it. Everyone turns to look. "Well, this must be the new girl," Miss Nagel says, smiling.

Miss Nagel is pretty like Aunt Lorraine. She has dark hair, blue eyes and red lips. She points to a seat on the other side of the room. "Come on in and join us. Say hello, class. This is Beverly Curtin."

Everyone says hello, and I say hello back. Then I turn to say goodbye to my mother and father, to kiss them and maybe even to go home with them because I don't want to stay here after all in this room full of people I don't know. But my mother and father have already turned to go. Mama says, "See you this afternoon," and that's it. They're walking down the hall with Mrs. Cormey, their backs toward me, and I am all alone standing in the doorway ready to cry because Mama didn't kiss me goodbye.

But I am too big to cry. I can't cry in front of everyone because they'll think I'm a crybaby, and I'm not. I'm just sad because Mama always kisses me goodbye. Mama always says "Give me a kiss," and I do, every day before school, after lunch and at night when it's bedtime. And I don't understand why she didn't say "Give me a kiss" this day, when this day is more important than lunch and bedtime.

I walk to my seat and try to hide there, but everyone keeps looking at me. Miss Nagel gives me a book, a piece of paper and a pencil, and then she goes to the front of the class. She's talking, but I don't know what she's saying because I feel like I've swallowed a balloon. I am trying so hard not to cry, trying harder than I've ever tried, but the tears are falling anyway.

The girl in front of me turns, looks, then turns away, and the boy beside me looks, too, but no one says anything. They're just letting me cry. And I think maybe I can sit here and cry just a little, and it will be OK. But then the girl in the row next to me and two seats up, a girl with reddish brown hair and brown eyes, turns around and sees me crying. She raises her hand and yells, "Miss Nagel! Miss Nagel! The new girl is crying!" Now I am really crying. I'm sobbing and Miss Nagel is beside me saying, "It's OK. It's OK, isn't it class?" and everyone's saying "Oh, please don't cry" and being so nice. But I know they think I'm a baby. I know that when they get home this afternoon they'll tell their mothers that there was a new girl in school today and that she cried. Then everyone will know I'm a baby, everyone in the whole town of Randolph.

"Why didn't you kiss me goodbye?" I ask my mother, when school finally ends. There they are outside in the car waiting for me, because this is a special day. After today I'll have to ride the bus like everyone else.

"You wanted me to kiss you? I thought you'd be embarrassed. That's why I didn't kiss you. Come here, and let me kiss you now," Mama says.

I climb into the front seat with them. Children are everywhere, walking home, getting on buses, but I don't care. I put my arms around my mother's neck and kiss her.

"Hey, don't I get one of those?" my father says and I kiss him, too, and I don't care who's looking.

Adventures in Paradise

The girl who told that I was crying is Janet Butler. She lives not across the street but across two streets. I can see her kitchen window from my front door. She didn't mean to tell on me, she says at the bus stop on my second day of school. Why were you crying anyway?

I don't tell her the real reason I cried. I say it's because I missed my friend Mary Toomey. Janet says, "Oh, I'll be your friend."

She stands with me at the bus stop and tells me who everyone is. That's Cora Sue Nelson, and that's her brother, Johnny Nelson, and she makes a face. That's Michelle Lyons, and that's Dottie Coty and that's Stanley Burwell. She makes another face. Whenever Janet says a boy's name she makes a face.

Janet saves a seat on the bus for me right beside her. When it's time for recess she says, "Wanna play Rattlesnake?" and takes my hand and drags me over to some girls who are singing a song I've never heard before.

"You don't know Rattlesnake?" Janet says.

"No."

"How come? What did you play at recess at your school?"

"We didn't have recess. We just had lunch."

"So what did you play at lunch?"

"I went home to lunch. We didn't play anything. We weren't allowed to play in the playground."

"R-A-T, T-L-E, S-N-A-K-E spells rattlesnake," the girls chant while holding hands in a line, twisting and turning just like a rattlesnake. I hold Janet's hand and sing and twist. The day is warm for February, and the sun is bright. I look at Janet, who is in front of me, and I think, this is fun. She is fun. And I look at all of the girls I don't know, and they don't scare me on this second day of school because Janet is my friend, and I like this game. I like playing outside and eating a bologna sandwich at my desk instead of walking all the way home for tomato soup. And Miss Nagel is in the schoolyard, too, not just to ring the bell or to tell the girls to stay away from the boys. She's walking in the grassy part of the field with two girls I don't know, and she's holding their hands. They are talking, and all of them are smiling.

At St. Joseph's, the only time a teacher holds your hand is when she's making sure you have it straight out before she hits you with the pointer. At St. Joseph's, the only snake we know is the one who made Eve eat the apple, and we would never make a game out of that.

I ride the bus home from my second day of school, and it's as if my first day of school was a long time ago.

The bus stops at Cora Sue Nelson's. I get off and walk with Janet to her house. She says, "Goodbye. See you tomorrow," and I hurry home to my house because I can't wait for tomorrow to play Rattlesnake again.

●   ●   ●   ●

Rosemary Jablonski and Jeannie Sullivan are best friends. That's what Janet tells me. That's why they are always together. That's why they don't play with anyone else. They walk side by side, their steps perfectly together as they stroll through the schoolyard. They sing songs together. They even have their own special hiding place behind a bush next to the side door of the school, which they call their clubhouse.

Most days at recess, unless it's raining and we have to stay indoors, Rosemary and Jeannie stroll around the playground, ending up at their clubhouse where they stand and whisper and giggle. Janet thinks they have their own special language, though it's hard to tell — they never talk to anyone but each other.

Rosemary is the smartest girl in second grade. Janet said smartness runs in Rosemary's family and that when Rosemary's sister was in second grade she got a double promotion.

"What's a double promotion?" I ask.

"It's when you're so smart you get to skip a grade. Rosemary's sister is so smart she went from grade two straight to grade four."

I have never heard of anyone being that smart. I think that Rosemary should get a double promotion, too. Whenever Miss Nagel asks a question, Rosemary knows the answer. She knows how to spell words like hippopotamus and rhinoceros. She knows how to subtract 54,896 from 72,612. She knows that there are forty-eight states, and she knows all of the capitals, and when Miss Nagel says, "Who can find Mississippi or Arkansas on the map?" Rosemary waves her hand.

I can see the back of Rosemary's head from where I sit. Her hair is blonde but darker than mine and as straight as mine is curly. Sometimes she turns around and looks at me; I smile, but she never smiles back. I don't think she likes me; but I like her, and I want to be her friend.

Sometimes I try to spy on her. I walk by the bush that is her clubhouse, and I pretend that my shoe is untied or that I've dropped a marble so that I can stop and listen to what she's saying to Jeannie. Sometimes they see me and yell "Go away!" Or Rosemary says, "Privacy," in a tone a grown-up would use.

I dream about being Rosemary's friend, walking through the schoolyard singing songs, hiding out behind the bush every day and saying "privacy" to people who walk by. I think that this would be even better than Rattlesnake and "Down in Mississippi where the boats go push." If I were Rosemary's friend everything would be perfect, and I wouldn't even mind the ghosts that come out at night and scare me.

I offer Rosemary my favorite marble. I tell her I like her red dress. I even give her half a Three Musketeers bar, but she doesn't say, "Want to play?" or "Want to come over to my house?" like Janet Butler does.

•   •   •   •

Mama buys me a First Holy Communion dress. My father drives us to Forest Hills, and we take the train into Boston and go right to Conrad and Chandler to the children's department. Mama buys me a dress, a veil, white shoes and white socks.

I go to Sunday school now. After Mass on Sundays, Janet and I walk to a big school on top of a hill where deaf children stay, even on weekends. We sit at these children's desks, and the sisters who teach the deaf children teach us about venial sin, mortal sin, original sin and actual sin. I already know about these things, but I have to go to Sunday school anyway.

After Sunday school Janet and all of her family drive to South Boston to where they used to live, and Janet visits her cousin Arlene. My father works on Sunday, so we don't drive anywhere. Mama and I watch movies on television. I love Sunday afternoons sitting on the couch with Mama. Sometimes when Lorraine gets a ride, she comes to visit, and when she does we eat Candy Cupboard chocolates while we watch TV. We always eat the whole box, and when my father gets home he says, "You didn't save any for me?" and pretends to be mad. But we know he is just fooling because he likes hermits and black-and-whites, not Candy Cupboard chocolates.

At Sunday school, we practice for our first confession. "In the name of the Father and of the Son and of the Holy Ghost," we say, while making the sign of the cross. "Bless me father, for I have sinned. This is my first confession."

We all practice together, but on our real first confession we will each say this alone.

• • • •

"Can you come out and play?" Janet says, standing at my back door. It's Saturday, not Sunday.

I put on my good coat over my old pants, and Mama says, "Don't wear that, Beverly. Wear your old coat," but my old one is tight and itches and is heavy, and I don't like it.

"I'll be careful, Mama. I won't get it dirty," I promise.

There are big holes all over the neighborhood and bigger piles of dirt right next to them. They're digging the foundation for more houses, my father has told me. I tell Janet this and she says, "I know that."

"So what do you want to do?" she asks me.

"I don't care," I say. "What do you want to do?"

"Let's have a race up to the top of that mountain. One, two, three, go," and she's off and running and has reached the top before I'm even halfway up the big mound of dirt.

"OK. This time I'll give you a head start," she says. "One, two, three, go," and I take off, and Janet counts to ten, but still she beats me to the top.

"Let's play tightrope," Janet says. We pretend that the trunks of trees lying on the ground are tightropes, and we walk on them. Then we pretend that the cement foundations are tightropes, and we walk on them, too. It's easy because they're not tightropes at all; they are wide pieces of cement. So we go back to running up the dirt hills, and finally, I beat her.

There's Janet at the bottom of the hill, not even halfway up, not even on the hill. I yell, "I'm king of the mountain!" and bang on my chest like Tarzan. Janet doesn't say anything, which isn't like her. "I'm king of the mountain!" I shout again, and still Janet stands as still as a statue in church. Then suddenly she jumps and screams, "Don't move. Don't move a muscle. There are snakes crawling through the dirt — millions, zillions of them. Rattlesnakes. They're everywhere."

I look down and see only dirt. I go to take a step, but she shrieks, "NO! NO!" and tells me to stand perfectly still, not even to breathe, because then they'll know I'm there. "I'll run and get help," she says, then bolts down Lewis Drive and around the corner until I can't see her anymore. Now I'm scared, because what if the snakes start crawling UP the mountain; what if they hear me breathing and are crawling UP the mountain now?

No one is around. No one lives here yet because there aren't any all-built houses, just foundations. And though it's spring, it's a cold Saturday morning; everyone's home watching "Sky King" inside warm houses, drinking cocoa and eating Girl Scout cookies far away from the snakes and the foundations where other snakes could be. And I am scared now, really, really scared. I am more scared than when the ghosts come out at night and pull my arms and legs, and try to carry me off with them back to their shimmery homes.

I wait for Janet to come back. I wait a long time. In my head I sing every song I know except "Rattlesnake" and I count to one hundred forward and backward. I say "The Lord's Prayer," and the "Hail Mary" and the "Act of Contrition," and still she's not back.

I can't scream, because the snakes will hear. I can't cry either because they'll hear that, too. So I just stand and think that any second they're going to wrap themselves around my legs and pull me into the dirt with them, and I'll be dead like Duffy.

Finally, Janet returns. She's walking down the street alone. She's munching on a pink Hostess Snowball. I wave, and she waves back. She shouts, "Why are you still up there?"

I can't shout because of the snakes. She knows that. So why is she asking me this?

She walks to the bottom of the dirt hill. "You didn't believe me about the snakes, did you? You haven't been up there that whole time? There aren't any rattlesnakes around here. Don't you know anything?"

I charge down the hill and push Janet as hard as I can. I say, "I never want to play with you again." And Janet says "So?" and pushes me, and I fall into a mud puddle.

"I don't want to play with you, either," she says, walking away while finishing her Hostess Snowball. "I was just fooling, you baby. Can't you take a joke?"

I go home angry and sad, with my good coat covered in mud.

The Catholic Hour

*L*ook. Here is my First Holy Communion book. Father Kelleher gave it to me. On the back are "God's Beautiful Ten Commandments." I know them all by heart. Mama cries when she helps me into my First Holy Communion dress. She says I look like a little angel. She bobby pins my veil to my hair, then makes me stand in the living room while she takes a picture. "Look solemn, Beverly," she says, "and fold your hands."

I try to do what she says, but I am so excited. My father has gone to Cambridge to get Little Nana, Big Nana and Aunt Lorraine, and I can't wait to see them. Here they come now. They're at the back door. Shane is barking. I hear Aunt Lorraine laughing.

"One more picture," Mama says, but I'm already running out of the living room, my new white patent leather shoes clicking on the floor. Little Nana cries when she sees me, too. She says I look like a bride. Big Nana's eyes get a happy look, and Lorraine just kneels and hugs me. My father says, "Give me the camera, Dot," and then he tells everyone to go outside because the light is better.

We are not supposed to talk in church or look at our families, smile, wave or do anything except concentrate on this Most Important Day in Our Life. We know this. But I am filing into church right behind Janet Butler, because we are in alphabetical order. I am seated in the same pew right next to her and when it's time to receive First Holy Communion, I follow right behind her.

We don't talk, because we aren't talking, but we look at one another. She smiles and I smile even though she pushed me in a puddle and ruined my good coat; even though my mother called her mother, and she got in trouble. I smile at my mother and father, and Janet turns and smiles at her mother and father and her two sisters. I think that all this smiling must be a sin, but it's hard not to smile when you're so happy because it's the Most Important Day of Your Life.

I kneel at the altar rail and close my eyes. When the

priest is standing in front of me, I stick out my tongue and receive Our Lord Jesus Christ. I think about how Jesus died for us and how Jesus gave us his body and blood in the sacrament of the Holy Eucharist. I stand and walk back to my pew knowing that I am holier now than I have ever been in my whole life.

After church, Big Nana gives me money. Aunt Lorraine gives me a book about saints. Vera Campbell, my mother's new friend and our next-door neighbor, gives me a kiss on the cheek. Little Nana gives me a pair of glow-in-the-dark rosary beads. I sit in the downstairs closet looking at them. They look like teeth, and I say a whole rosary before I come out.

The next day I receive Holy Communion again with my parents at Mass, and the same thing happens. I feel holy all over, all the way down to my toes. I think that Janet must, too, because she starts sitting with me on the bus again. She doesn't call me scaredy-cat or tattletale, and at lunch she gives me one of her Hostess Snowballs.

Big Nana, Shane and me

Those Two

*M*ama says that Aunt Lorraine has a boyfriend and that she's bringing him over to meet us.

Aunt Lorraine has a boyfriend? So, Aunt Lorraine has lots of boyfriends. When I walk down Central Square with Aunt Lorraine, men always stop and talk to her. The flower man, Joe the keyman, the man who sells newspapers and comic books, the meat man, the fruit man. Aunt Lorraine is so beautiful they can't help but look at her and then fall head-over-heels in love with her. She doesn't have just one boyfriend. She has lots and lots of boyfriends. And she's so nice she likes all of them. But Aunt Lorraine says she loves only me.

Mama says, "I think she might love this boyfriend, Beverly. I think it's serious." But I don't believe her.

I wait at the dining room window, watching Janet Butler, Michelle Lyons and Ann Marie Tantillo play freeze tag. It's August, and though it's night, it's still light out. It's hot, too, too hot to sit in the breezeless inside. Mama says, "Why don't you go out and play. Waiting won't make Lorraine get here any faster."

But I want to wait. I want to see this boyfriend the minute he gets here. I want to see if Aunt Lorraine sits close to him in the car and if he opens her door. Then I'll know if she loves him and if he loves her.

But, they pull up to the front of the house when I'm in the bathroom, so I don't get to see him in the car after all. All of a sudden he's here in our kitchen, dressed all in white: white shoes, pants, shirt and hat, his arm around my aunt's waist. He's smiling at everyone as if he expects us to like him, as if anyone could like a man who dresses like Popeye and looks like Liberace.

"This is Frank," Lorraine says, and I think, Frank? I hate the name Frank. But Lorraine must love it because it's practically the only word she says. "Frank comes from Lexington. Frank went to school there. Frank is in the Coast Guard. Frank says this. Frank does that. What do you think, Frank? Frank. Frank. Frank." My beautiful, wonderful, absolutely perfect Aunt Lorraine has had a spell cast on her by some wicked witch because she's acting as if Frank is a prince.

We don't eat Candy Cupboard chocolates and watch TV. We don't sit at the kitchen table and drink coffee. Lorraine doesn't let me paint her fingernails red, and she doesn't ask if I want her to paint mine. And when she kisses me goodbye and leaves, it's as if she were never here to begin with.

"He's a very nice boy, Beverly," Mama says, tucking me into bed. "You're not giving him a chance. You're jealous. You want your Aunt Lorraine all to yourself, but that's not fair to her, you know. Just because she loves him, doesn't mean she loves you any less. I love your father and you, don't I?"

Mama kisses me, shuts off the light and walks down the stairs. I lie in my bed and think, am I jealous? Is that what this is? I can't remember what Sister Joseph Agnes said about jealousy, but I think it's like envy and pride and a very bad thing. I think jealousy is one of those sins that turns your soul black.

I reach under my pillow and get my glow-in-the-dark rosary beads, and I hold them in front of me. The skeletons don't come anymore. Not since my First Holy Communion day. I think the rosary beads scared them away.

I hum a song Mama sings: "When you're worried and you can't sleep, just count your blessings instead of sheep, and you'll fall asleep, counting your blessings." I think about Frank and how there has to be something about him that I like, some blessing.

I liked when he left. I liked when he said he wouldn't see us for a while because he was going to sea for two months. I liked when Aunt Lorraine turned to me and said, "I'll see you next week, Baybo. I want to help you pick out your new back-to-school clothes."

Maybe when we're together next week I can tell her how much I miss her, how I wish we could see each other, more and how I want to stay at Big Nana's with her before school starts. Maybe we'll have so much fun together that she'll forget all about Frank.

Beverly Beckham

Aunt Lorraine and Frank

On Your Way

I don't like Miss Collins, I don't like my seat in the back of the room, I don't like third grade and I can't wait for this day to be over so I can go home.

Miss Collins says, "Please stand, class, while we recite the 'Pledge of Allegiance.' " Then she tells us that the President of the United States changed the words and that now we have to say "one nation, under God, indivisible," instead of just "one nation indivisible." I don't believe her.

Miss Collins says that we will sing a song today because it's the first day of school, but that we won't sing a song every day after the "Pledge of Allegiance" because singing is a waste of time.

Mama says that singing is never a waste of time. Mama says that the Seven Dwarfs are right, that singing always makes things better. Whistle while you work, and the work gets done before you know it. Mama always puts her favorite songs on our new record player when she dusts and vacuums. She sings along, and she swears that singing even makes cleaning the house fun.

Today we sing the words "Oh beautiful for spacious skies" and I look around the room to see whose voice is leading the way. Of course, it's Rosemary's. It isn't fair that Rosemary is smart and pretty, that she has straight hair instead of ugly curly hair, that she has a seat in the front of the class and that she has a pretty voice, too.

I watch the clock on the wall move slowly toward ten, eleven, then noon, but lunch isn't any fun either. Miss Collins says we're not to talk while we eat. "Eat, and then you can talk." I buy milk, and it's warm. I unwrap my tuna fish sandwich, and it's warm, too. The bread is soggy, and I wish more than anything that I were anywhere but here.

Finally, it's time to go outside. "Put on your sweaters and jackets, boys and girls," Miss Collins orders, then stands at the door to make sure we do as she says. I file out in back of everyone else. When at last I get outside, my whole class is gone, running to the swing sets in the back of the playground.

It's a warm day. It feels like summer. I want to take off my sweater, but there's Miss Collins watching, so I keep it on. My sweater itches, my new shoes hurt, and though I am outside in the fresh air, I feel trapped.

I see Rosemary walking through the field, walking, not in a hurry, but sort of strolling along. I wonder, where is Jeannie Sullivan? I think about the rows of boys and girls and about where everyone is sitting and I try to picture Jeannie Sullivan, but I can't. Maybe she isn't in school today. Maybe she's sick. Maybe today Rosemary will talk to me.

I run over to Rosemary, and I say, "Hi!" and she says "Hi" back. I say, "Where are you going?" and she says, "Nowhere," and I say, "Oh." Then we sort of start walking to nowhere together. Rosemary is so beautiful and so smart that I can't believe I am actually walking around the schoolyard with her.

"You have hair just like a doll I have at home," Rosemary says, and I wonder, does she like the doll? Does she keep it on her bed for everyone to see? Or is it an ugly doll that is hidden in a drawer?

"Does your mother curl your hair in the morning or at night?" Rosemary asks.

I say, "She doesn't curl it. It curls itself, and I don't like it. It's too short and frizzy. I wish I had your hair."

Rosemary says her mother curls her hair every morning with a curling iron, but the curls never stay put, no matter how much spray her mother uses.

"What's a curling iron?" I ask before I can stop myself. I want to take back the words because I don't want Rosemary to think I'm so stupid that I don't know what a curling iron is.

Rosemary says a curling iron is a long, hot thing that you wrap your hair around and that burns your scalp and your neck, too.

"Oh," I say, still not understanding.

I want to ask Rosemary to come over to my house to play, but I think she'll say no because tomorrow Jeannie Sullivan will be here. Then she won't talk to me anymore. I think, how I wish Jeannie Sullivan would stay away forever so that I could talk to Rosemary every day, so that we could be best friends.

I don't mean to ask about Jeannie Sullivan but I do. It's like she's right here in the middle of us, and I can't ignore her. So I say, "Where is Jeannie Sullivan?" Rose looks sad suddenly, and I wish I hadn't wished that Jeannie Sullivan would stay away forever because Jeannie Sullivan is Rosemary's best friend. I know how it is to lose a best friend, because I lost Mary Toomey.

"She moved," Rose says.

"Moved? Moved where?"

"Across town. She's going to another school."

Rose is sad, really, really sad, and I am sad, too. But part of me is so glad I want to jump up and down. Now, maybe Rosemary will walk around the schoolyard with me every day. And now maybe we can play on the see-saw together and sing songs and tell secrets behind the bush where Rose says, "Privacy."

"Do you want to come over to my house tomorrow?" Rosemary asks. I say, "Yes, I'd love to," even though I have to ask my mother first and even though I don't know where Rosemary lives.

"I'll call you after school, so my mother can talk to your mother," Rose says. "Where do you live?" she asks.

I tell her my address and give her my phone number. When it's time to line up and file back into school, I'm smiling because I don't hate third grade anymore. I love third grade. I love the new "Pledge of Allegiance." I love my seat in the back of the class. I love practicing the Rhinehart method, doing my penmanship over and over because Miss Collins says I don't know how to make small R's. I love the hot day, my itchy sweater and my tight shoes. When the day is over and Rosemary says, "See you tomorrow," I can't wait for tomorrow, because I know now, I am positively sure, that third grade is going to be the best grade so far.

Grade 3 — Tower Hill School

People are Funny

Frank is back from sea, and he is in my kitchen again, this time dressed in a navy blue sailor suit. Aunt Lorraine is standing next to him looking at him as if he is a statue of the Blessed Virgin come to life.

"Frank suggested that we take a ride to Randolph," Lorraine says. "Frank thought it would be fun to surprise you. Frank said it was too nice a night to stay in the city. Frank said he's going to teach me how to drive."

Everyone walks into the parlor, Lorraine holding Frank's hand as if she is afraid he might get lost on the way. I wish he would get lost. Then I think, no, that's being jealous. And being jealous is a sin.

I try hard to see Frank through Lorraine's eyes. That's what Mama said I should do. So I look at Frank and pretend I'm Lorraine, but I still can't figure out why she gets all sweet and mushy and sickening around him.

What I see when I look at him, no matter whose eyes I use, is Liberace. I wish I liked Liberace. Then it wouldn't be so bad having your aunt date someone who looks like a famous piano player. But I don't like him, Liberace or Frank, and when Lorraine says, "You're being awfully quiet, Baybo. What are you thinking?" it just spills out that I'm thinking that Frank looks like Liberace.

Lorraine, my father and Frank laugh because they like Liberace, and they think I must, too. So they think I like Frank. Mama is the only one who knows the truth.

At school I play with Rosemary every day. We walk around the playground arm in arm. We teach each other our favorite songs. We whisper behind the bush, which is now our clubhouse. I tell Rosemary about Frank, and she says she doesn't understand why some girls get dopey over boys. She says she will never, ever be that way. I say I won't either, and we make a pact, curling our little fingers together and shutting our eyes.

After school I sometimes go to Rosemary's. I would go every afternoon if I could, because I love Rosemary's house. In her kitchen Rose has her own special drawer full of construction paper and glue, and in her yard, which is as big as a field, she has a swing that her father made and hung between two trees. It's a big wooden swing with a long seat, and we ride on it together. We sing songs while we pump and make up stories. When we get tired, we go inside, and Rose's mother makes us tuna fish sandwiches and chocolate milk.

Rosemary has a big cellar, a fat cat and a real piano, which she plays with two fingers. There is always something fun to do at Rose's house. But Mama says I can't go every day no matter how much I want to, because I have to be careful not to wear out my welcome.

"What does 'wear out my welcome' mean, Mama?"

"It means that people will get tired of you if they see you too much. It means you shouldn't go over there all the time."

I don't think I'm wearing out my welcome, so I ask Rosemary. Her mother hears me and says, "What? Where would you ever get an idea like that?" And I tell her my mother said it.

"You're not wearing out your welcome," Mrs. Jablonski assures me. "I like having you here."

I go home and tell my mother this, but she says Mrs. Jablonski is just being polite.

Rosemary knows lots of things about the Bible. She teaches me, "For God so loved the world that he gave his only begotten son for who shall ever believeth in him shall not perish but have life everlasting." She says, "That's John. Chapter: 3. Verse: 16."

"Who's John?"

"John's one of the apostles."

I know about Peter, but I don't know about John. "How come you know this?" I ask Rose.

"Because it's in the Bible," she says.

In Rosemary's house, there is a big Bible in the living room on the coffee table full of birthdays, death days and pictures of God, Jesus and holy looking people I don't know. We don't have a Bible in our house. I ask my mother why, and she says we have missals and priests, so we don't need a Bible. But Rosemary says everyone needs a Bible because it is the word of God.

Rosemary isn't Catholic. She's Baptist, which means that she does not believe in the one true, holy Catholic and apostolic church. I'm supposed to pity her because she hasn't been baptized and if she should die suddenly she'll go to Limbo with all the other unbaptized children and never see the face of God because her soul is marked by original sin. But I don't pity Rose. She gets to watch cartoons in Sunday school, color pictures, eat cookies and sing songs and put on plays. She has so much fun in Sunday school that she likes Sundays.

She teaches me one of the songs: "Oh be careful little eyes what you see, oh be careful little eyes what you see. For the Father up above is looking down with love; so be careful little eyes what you see."

The song goes on and on: "Oh be careful little ears what you hear. Be careful little mouth what you say. Be careful little feet where you go," and it's such a fun song that we sing it over and over and act it out too, covering our eyes and our mouths with our hands.

I teach Rose what I learn at Sunday school, but it isn't like singing. We play confession and pretend Communion with white Necco wafers, but I can't make it feel the way real Communion does. So I don't mind that we play Baptist Sunday school more than Catholic Sunday school; I love listening to Rose recite words from the Bible, and I like listening to the songs she sings. "Maybe you can come to church with me," she says, and I ask Mama. But Mama says I can't, because there is only one true church, and we have to go there.

"Maybe Rose can come with us, then?" But Mama shakes her head. "Sorry, Baybo. She can't."

So I don't see Rose on Sundays. I go to church and Sunday school with Janet, and then I come home and watch TV with Mama.

"What do you do on Sundays?" I ask Rose. She says after church she goes to her grandmother's or her Aunt Lillian's, or her Aunt Lillian comes to her house.

I wish Aunt Lorraine came to my house on Sundays, but she never does because she's out with Frank. She'd like it here. Mama pulls down the shades and makes it like nighttime in the parlor. We sit on the green couch, eat candy or ice cream and watch sad stories about pretty ladies who have terrible things happen to them. Mama always cries watching these movies. I say, "Why are you crying Mama? It's only a movie?" She sniffles and says, "You're too young to understand," and I wish I were older so that I could understand and cry, too.

It's Magic

*A*t Brownies we are getting ready to fly up. Fly up means that next year we'll be Girl Scouts. Girl Scouts wear green uniforms and get a gold Girl Scout pin. Brownies wear brown uniforms and aren't as important as Girl Scouts.

I love Brownies. Mrs. Barnes, Deborah Barnes' mother, is our Brownie leader. Every week when we go to her house, we eat cookies she makes. Sometimes they're still in the oven when we get there. We watch her take them out of the oven, and we grab them and eat them while they're hot, even before she can put them on a plate.

Sometimes, after we eat our cookies, when the weather's nice, we do outside projects. Mrs. Barnes helps us collect leaves and grasses and she tells us the names of these things and shows us how to tie knots so they don't come undone.

Sometimes, on stormy days, we do science experiments in the house. Today we are planting seeds in empty egg cartons. We brought the egg cartons from home, but Mrs. Barnes has the seeds and a big can full of dirt.

I plant bachelor buttons, Rosemary plants morning glories. Janet Butler plants both. I wish I had thought of that. It's fun sticking the tiny seeds in the dirt, looking at the pictures on the packages and knowing that in a few months our egg cartons will be full of pretty flowers. I like planting seeds in an egg carton, but I don't like planting them in the ground where there are worms, ants and spiders. When my flowers get big I'm going to give them to my mother so she can plant them in our garden.

After we finish planting we wash our hands. Mrs. Barnes tells us to sit in a big circle, and we talk about flying up. She says we're going to have to practice, that the most important practice will be on a Saturday morning at St. Bernadette's Hall, and that we must all make an effort to be there because flying up is a big moment in our lives. Then she asks how many of us are going to march in the Memorial Day parade. We all raise our hands because we can't wait to march in a parade through the center of town. Mrs. Barnes is going to march with us.

Then Mrs. Barnes tells us that she won't be our troop leader next year, that when we're Girl Scouts we will have a different leader. We say, "We want you, Mrs. Barnes," and it's not just words. We do. Mrs. Barnes never yells if we get cookie crumbs on the floor or if someone doesn't tie her knot right or forgets the Girl Scout Pledge. Mrs. Barnes was supposed to fly up with us. "Why aren't you flying up, Mrs. Barnes? Why can't you be our leader?"

Rosemary tells me after Brownies, as we walk up Althea Road carefully carrying our egg cartons, that Mrs. Barnes is getting a baby; that's why she isn't flying up.

"A baby? How do you know that, Rose?"

"Because my mother said."

I want to turn around, go back to Mrs. Barnes and ask her where she's getting the baby and if they have any extras because my mother wants one, too. I tell Rose this, and she just looks at me.

I think maybe Rosemary doesn't know about Moses and how he came, so I tell her how I know that babies come in a basket and float down a stream, but that I don't know where the special streams are. "That's the problem, Rose. But Mrs. Barnes must know because she has three children and now she's getting another one."

Rosemary tells me that babies don't come in baskets and don't float down streams. "They grow inside mothers," she says. "They grow like seeds."

Seeds? I understand about seeds. My mother said Mrs. Lyons swallowed a watermelon seed; that's why her stomach grew so big. You have to be careful not to swallow seeds because you could grow watermelons, oranges and grapefruits inside you. Then you have to go to the hospital and have your stomach cut open to get them out. But I didn't know about baby seeds.

"Are you sure, Rose?"

Rose says she's positive. I ask where do you get baby seeds. Rose says she doesn't know, but she thinks God plants them.

If God plants them, why isn't a baby growing inside my mother? She talks to God all the time. She even has a statue of God in a dress on her bureau. I think about God, the seed, Moses and the basket, and I don't know what to believe. I know Rosemary is the smartest girl in school, but Mama said that Moses was found in a stream; so maybe there are two ways of getting a baby.

"Maybe," Rose says. "But I know Mrs. Barnes' baby is growing inside her, and I know my Aunt Lillian had a baby growing inside her."

I ask God to plant a seed in my mother. I add it to my list of prayers at night. Please, God, please, please, please, please, I say one hundred times.

And I wait for my mother's stomach to grow.

Janet Butler

Can You Top This?

*M*ama is always talking about someday, when her ship comes in.

"Someday, when my ship comes in, I'm going to buy a dining room table with four matching chairs," she says. "Someday when my ship comes in I'm going to buy your father a new car with whitewall tires, and I'll get you a bureau with a mirror, and we'll have the fanciest wallpaper, and the thickest rugs, and crystal lamps, and velvet drapes, and we'll finish the upstairs and the cellar, and we'll go on vacation, maybe even to California."

Mama sighs when she talks about her ship and gets a sad look in her eyes. I don't blame her. Her ship has been a long time at sea. I imagine it's like Ali Baba's cave, full of silver, gold, diamonds, rubies and pearls, stolen by some pirates and now adrift, waiting for a wind to bring it home.

I ask Mama when was the last time she saw her ship. She says last night in her dreams. She laughs, but her eyes are still sad, and I don't understand why. I think we should tell Frank to look for Mama's ship because he's in the Coast Guard and that's what he does, but Mama says he doesn't look for ships like hers.

Mrs. Jablonski mustn't have a ship, because she never says, "Someday, when my ship comes in," and neither does Mrs. Butler or Mrs. Tantillo or Mrs. Barnes. I think we must be the only ones to have a big ship full of treasures out at sea, and I wonder why we're so lucky and no one else is.

• • • •

Rosemary's cat had kittens, and we're looking at them, touching their soft fur and holding them in our hands. I want a kitten so much, but I can't have one because I have a dog.

It's almost Christmas and Rosemary's house is all decorated. The tree in her parlor looks as if it belongs to an angel. It's not decorated like our tree with different colored lights, ornaments and tinsel. Her tree is soft and dreamy looking, covered with a big white cloud that Rose says will cut you if you touch it because it's made of spun glass.

I think it is the most beautiful tree I have ever seen. Rose says it takes a long time to put angel hair on a tree. I say, "Angel hair? You mean that's hair from a real angel?"

"Of course not," Rose says, looking at me as if I were a first-grader. Then she goes and gets a package of angel hair. I touch it even though I'm not supposed to. It feels like thread and cotton candy, soft but sharp, too. Rose says, "Now you have to wash your hands because you don't want to get that stuff in your eyes." So I do.

Rose knows everything.

She says, "Let's sing Christmas songs." We start with "Rudolph the Red-Nosed Reindeer" and "Santa Claus is Coming to Town." Then she sings, "The-e fir-rst no-o-el," and I say, "I don't know that." She says, "What do you mean you don't know that? Everyone knows that. You sing it at church."

"Not at my church," I say.

"Well, do you sing, 'We Three Kings of Orient Are?' "

"No."

" 'Silent Night?' "

"No."

" 'Joy to the World?' "

"No."

"What do you sing?"

I tell her about "Tantum Ergo, Sacramentum," and she says, "Is that a Christmas song?" I say, "I don't think so," because we sing it all the time, not just at Christmas. We sing "Holy God We Praise Thy Name," too. But Rose says that songs you sing all the time aren't special, not like Christmas carols, and what kind of a church is the Catholic church anyway if they don't let you sing Christmas songs?

She teaches me "The First Noel" while we play with the kittens, and we sing it as we walk around the schoolyard the next day. I tell my mother that "The First Noel" is my new favorite song, and she says, "That's good, Beverly." I ask, "Why don't we sing Christmas carols at our church?" She says, "Because in our church we do more praying than singing."

I know that our church is the one true Catholic and apostolic church, that Rosemary's church isn't the one true church and that the people who go there may be very nice people but we should pray for their souls anyway so that before they die they become Catholic and are saved.

But I feel funny praying for Rosemary's soul. She's the one who taught me to pray to God for things like good grades and help on a test. She says she prays every night. First she says, "Now I lay me down to sleep, I pray the Lord my soul to keep. If I should die before I wake, I pray the Lord my soul to take." Then she says, "God bless my mother and father and sister and brother and grandparents and aunts and cousins." And then she says, "Please, God, please, let me get an 'A' on my spelling test tomorrow, please, pretty please, and let Miss Collins pick me to be in charge of the room." And if Rose wants something really special, she says please one hundred times.

God must like hearing all those pleases because he listens to Rosemary's prayers. She gets an 'A' on every test, and she is always the one Miss Collins picks to be in charge when she leaves the room. I try saying please one hundred times but I always lose count. I figure that's why Miss Collins never leaves me in charge of the room.

• • • •

At Brownies, we make Christmas ornaments for our parents. We use Styrofoam balls, sequins and common pins. I make my ball red and silver.

At school, we make Christmas cards. I draw a Christmas tree, and then I draw my father, my mother, Shane and me. On the inside I write "Merry Christmas, Love, Beverly." Miss Collins makes me do the whole thing over because she says I am supposed to be writing the Rhine-hart way, not the Palmer way, and my card is sloppy.

Everyone goes out to recess while I stay inside redoing my card. It's a cold day, but the sun is warm and bright. From the closed window I watch Rosemary playing jump rope with Janet, Ann Marie and Ginny Coty. Miss Collins says, "Stop looking out the window and get your work done," so I do, but she still isn't happy with my card. After lunch I have to stay in and do it again. Miss Collins says, "Let's see if you can get it right this time, Miss Curtin."

I think it's funny being called Miss Curtin. No one has ever called me Miss Curtin in my whole life, so I smile. Miss Collins says, "Do you think this is funny? Do you think I enjoy spending my free time in this room babysitting you?" And I say "Oh, no, Miss Collins. I wasn't smiling about that. I was thinking about something else."

She ignores what I said. She sits at her desk and corrects papers. I draw the tree again and my family. But I shorten the message on the inside to "Love, Bev." If I stay away from R's, my writing is fine.

Recess is over by the time I'm finished. Two more hours until it's time to go home. I can't wait. We have penmanship, then geography, then music. It's during music that Miss Collins says, "How many of you still believe in Santa Claus? Raise your hand."

I believe, and I know Rosemary believes. Janet Butler definitely believes, but not one of us raises our hand. There's not a hand raised in the entire class, though I know practically everyone believes in Santa Claus because, of course, we believe. Who else would bring us toys?

"Well, it's good that you all know the truth. Now I'm going to tell you how the myth began."

Myth? A myth is like unicorns, dragons and leprechauns. A myth is like a story that people make up. Why is Miss Collins saying that Santa Claus is a myth?

"Miss Collins says that Santa Claus is a myth," I tell my

mother the second I get home from school. "Is she right?"

My mother is standing at the kitchen sink peeling pota-toes for dinner. She has on a brown and white housedress with an apron over it. She stops peeling, wipes her hands on the apron and turns to me.

"Miss Collins told you there's no Santa?"

"That's what she said. Is she right?"

"How did she tell you?"

"She said he's a myth. She said parents invented him. Is this true?"

"Of course it's not true. Do you think you'd get any presents if there were no Santa Claus? We can't afford presents? Who do you think brings them?"

"I think Santa Claus brings them, Mama."

But I wonder why Miss Collins would say such a thing.

Time Will Tell

*L*ittle Nana is visiting. My parents are somewhere, not home, and Little Nana is watching me. My mother said before she left, "Don't let her stay up all night, Kay, she needs her sleep. And don't let her eat a lot of candy." And Little Nana said, "I won't, Dot. You just go out and have yourself a good time, and don't worry about us. We'll be fine."

They backed out of the driveway and Little Nana sighed, lit a cigarette and said, "Your mother worries too much, you know that? Want a Chiclet?"

I eat a box of Chiclets. I chew one until it loses its flavor. Then I chew another and do the same thing until they're gone. Little Nana never says, "You've had enough. You're going to rot your teeth." She says, "Here. You can have the package. You can chew them all now, or you can save some until later. It doesn't matter. When they're gone, they're gone."

Little Nana puts me to bed at 7:30 just like Mama said, but she stays upstairs with me and tells me story after story until it's 8:30. She tells the best stories about two boys and two girls who are friends, but who are detectives, too. They have a clubhouse in the city park hidden way up in a tree so no one knows it's there. They are always having adventures and always helping people in trouble. The best thing is that they go to school and are just kids, and no one knows about their secret, important lives.

Nana tucks me in, kisses me good night and says, "See you in the morning," because she always sleeps over when she babysits. Then she goes downstairs and watches the end of "The Jackie Gleason Show."

I watch "The Jackie Gleason Show," too, from my hiding spot on the stairs. Nana says, "Why don't you come down and sit on the couch next to me where it's more comfortable?" and I do. We sit and watch TV together until it's 11 and time for my parents to come home.

• • • •

Everyone is coming for Christmas, our first Christmas in our new house. My father picks up Little Nana early Christmas Eve, and she sits at the kitchen table, drinks port wine and watches Mama stuff the turkey.

I get to stay up late because Big Nana has to work and won't get here until past midnight. My father has to pick her up, too.

The house smells and tastes like Christmas. For the first time, I get to have a sip of port wine in my own glass. Big Nana says a sip will never hurt you, and Mama doesn't argue. Mama never argues with Big Nana.

In bed, I keep my eyes open because I know Santa has to come soon. It's late, only a few hours until morning, and I want to see Santa this year so I can tell Rose, Janet and Miss Collins that I saw him with my own eyes.

They think it's their mothers who leave the toys. They think Miss Collins was right, but I know she lied because my mother never would. So I stay perfectly still; I don't even wriggle my toes. It's so warm and comfortable in my bed that my eyes want to close, but I tell them no, they have to stay open.

My room is pretty now. My father covered all the scary silver paper with wood, and then he wallpapered over the wood. Then Frank came over and told my father how he could make the floor in my room look nice, too. Together, they used big wood squares and made a diamond shape in the middle of the room.

The very best thing my father did was put speakers in the walls. Now when I turn on my record player, the music comes from everywhere. "Your father is so smart," Janet said. "This is great." It is great, and I love it, but tonight I don't listen to music. I listen for Santa.

I hear the jingle bells before I see them. It's so quiet that I can't hear the Nanas in the next room or my mother and father downstairs. All I hear are bells, distant at first, but getting closer, like a phone when you hurry to answer it. And then, when the bells are so loud that I think they'll

wake up the Nanas, I see the sleigh and the reindeer outside my window.

They're flying by. They're going to Ann Marie's house.
I see them stop and land on her roof, and I watch them
from my bed. Santa gets out of the sleigh and disappears
with a sack full of toys on his back, and the reindeer sit
on the roof.

I can't wait to tell everyone what I saw. I think that I
will never sleep now and that I will never be able to pretend to be asleep when Santa comes. I am so excited that
I fear Santa will hear my heart beating all the way from
downstairs.

So I try to slow my heart. I try to take quiet breaths —
the way cowboys do when Indians are near. I close my
eyes and pretend to sleep, and I pretend as hard as I can
so that Santa won't know I'm pretending. The next thing
I know it's bright in my room, and it's morning, Christmas
morning. Mama is singing from the bottom of the steps,
"Lazy Mary, will you get up, will you get up?" And I bolt
out of bed and race down the stairs.

Medic

Mama says, "Eat your egg while it's hot." But I don't want to eat my egg. I don't want to eat anything.

"Eat that egg, Beverly. This is the last time I'm going to tell you." So I eat it; I force it down. It's cold, and the yellow part is runny.

I go to my room. I want to be in my bed — beside my stuffed dog that Little Nana gave me a long time ago — with the white spread and its white nubbies covering me. I don't want to do anything but lie down and go to sleep.

It's a warm spring day, and the window is wide open, but I close it and pull down the shade because the air feels cold on my skin and the bright light hurts my eyes. But then, with the window closed, the room feels like the back seat of a car, stuffy and small; all I can think of is that fried egg, and all I can taste is that egg. So I open the window again, pull up the shade, climb under the covers and shiver.

Mama comes upstairs and says, "Are you all right, Baybo?" and places her hand on my forehead. I say, "I'm fine," because I am now, in my bed under my covers. But I'm shivering as I'm talking, so she walks downstairs to get a thermometer.

Later she brings me a Coke, but I don't want it. Then she brings me coffee ice cream, but I don't want that, either. "Have some water," Mama says, but I don't want water.

"You have to drink something, Beverly."

"I don't want to drink, Mama. I just want to sleep."

"She has a temperature," I hear her tell someone. "No, she won't drink anything. I tried, but she won't even have a sip of Coke."

A doctor is in my room, at the foot of my bed. He looks more like a teacher than a doctor. He doesn't have a beard or gray hair, and he doesn't frown when he says hello. He opens his black bag and takes out that thing he sticks in his ears so he can hear my heart beating. Then he puts a Popsicle stick on my tongue, tells me to say

"Aahh" and shines a small flashlight down my throat. I think, I don't have a flashlight in my Nurse Nancy kit. Maybe flashlights are just for doctors. I want to ask him this, but he presses my stomach, and it hurts. Then he takes the flashlight and looks in my eyes. That hurts, too.

He says I need to go to the hospital and Mama says, "Is it serious?" and they go out of the room and I can't hear them anymore.

They put me in a crib in the hospital. I'm not a baby. Why do I need a crib?

"It's not a crib, Baybo. It's just so you won't fall out," Mama says.

But it is a crib. It has big iron bars, and they're so high I couldn't climb out if I wanted to.

I don't like the hospital. It's too bright and white and noisy, and the nurse isn't Nurse Nancy. She's mean. She tells my mother and father, "You really must go now." I yell, "No! No! Don't leave me."

But they say, "We have to, honey. You need your rest."

There's a small television near my crib. My father says, "How about if you watch a little TV until you get sleepy?" and he is all ready to put a quarter in the TV because you have to pay to watch it in the hospital. "Isn't that funny, Beverly? It's like a juke box," my father says.

But the mean nurse says, "That's not a good idea, Mr. Curtin. Really, you must go."

"Later, then," my father tells me, "when we come back. We'll be back by seven, and we'll watch 'You Asked For It.' OK?"

I have my Cinderella watch, so I know what time it is. It is three in the afternoon. They'll be back at seven. That's four hours. I love "You Asked For It." I love how people can write and ask to see something, and then they put it on TV.

"OK, Dad," I say. "But promise you'll come back?"

"I promise," he says and crosses his heart.

My mother and father kiss me goodbye. They say, "See

you in a little while," and I watch them walk away out of the big room. I am brave and don't say anything until they are just about to disappear. Then I yell, "No! Don't go! Don't go!" because I don't want to stay here. I want to go home with them. I'm scared and I'm in a crib like a baby. I'm hot, I'm cold, and my stomach hurts.

"Mama, Mama!" I scream, and they both turn around. But the nurse says, "Really, you must leave. I'll take care of this." Mama throws me a kiss and says, "Be a good girl, Beverly," and my father says, "We'll be back at seven." Then they are gone.

I am not a good girl. I cry and cry and then I sleep. When I wake it's dark and quiet, and I'm alone. I look at my watch, but I can't see what time it is because it's dark in the room. I know that "You Asked For It" is over and that my parents didn't come.

I stand up and try to get out of my cage, but I can't. It's too high. So I shout, "Mama! Mama!" and someone comes, a different nurse, and says, "Well, hello, sleepy head. I was beginning to wonder if you were going to sleep through breakfast, too."

"I want my mother," I say between tears.

"She'll be back. She was here, but you weren't. You were off in dreamland. Why are you crying, honey? Don't cry."

"They didn't come. They said they'd come, but they didn't. Why didn't they?"

"Yes, they did. They came, and they made sure you were OK, and they tucked in your blanket. Look, they even left a quarter beside your bed. See? In case you woke up and wanted to watch TV."

There is a quarter on the table next to a glass of water. They must have come. But why didn't they wake me? I wanted to see them. I wanted them to take me home. I want to go home now.

"You'll be going home soon," the nurse says. "And they'll be back soon. Are you hungry? Do you want something to eat? How would you like some orange juice and some toast? And how would you like a lollipop while you're waiting. Your parents brought those, too."

The nurse opens a drawer in the table, and it's full of red lollipops, my favorite. They did come. The nurse wasn't lying. They didn't forget me.

• • • •

I can eat all the lollipops I want. I can eat lollipops and drink Coke, even if it's almost time for supper. That's what the doctor says. I tell the doctor and the nurses that it was the fried egg that made me sick, but they don't believe me. They pat me on the head and say things like, "Oh, is that right, dear?" And then they go on with their conversations.

Mama tells me, "It wasn't the fried egg that made you sick, Beverly, but if you don't like fried eggs, you don't have to eat them anymore."

No more fried eggs and all the Coke I can drink. I am beginning to feel much, much better.

I go home, but I can't go back to school. I don't understand why. I want to go to school. I miss both Rosemary and Janet.

Mama watches "Ding Dong School" with me. Miss Frances says, "Boys and girls, go get your mothers," so I do, and though she is defrosting the refrigerator she comes and sits next to me and watches until Miss Frances sings the goodbye song. Mama sings as she defrosts and as she dusts and does the dishes. She sings a song I've never heard before: "Go-ho, go-ho, go-ho. Oh let me go-ho, let me go-ho, let me go, lover."

I ask Mama if I can call Rosemary after school, and she says, "Yes, you may." Mama says a phone is not a toy, so I'm not allowed to use it except when I ask. I can't wait to talk to Rose. I haven't talked to her since before I went to the hospital. But I have to wait even longer, because we have a party line, which means we have to share it with the Cotys who live down the street. Mrs. Coty is on

the phone when I pick it up. I have to be polite, not interrupt and not keep picking up the phone, because that's
rude. And I must never, ever listen to what Mrs. Coty is
saying on the telephone, because you have to respect
people's privacy.

I understand all about privacy because Rosemary and
I wouldn't want anyone listening to our private conversations behind the bush at school. But Mrs. Coty will not
get off the phone. I pick it up. I hear her voice. I hang up
the phone and count to sixty. Then I pick up the phone,
hang it up and count to sixty again. I do this over and
over. I don't mean to listen to what she's saying. I only
want to listen a little to see if she's even close to saying
goodbye because I am dying to talk to Rose. But it's hard
to tell from just a few words. So, finally, I put the phone
to my ear, stay very still and try not to breathe.

But Mrs. Coty must have excellent ears because she
knows I'm there. She says, "Who's on the phone? Who's
listening to me?" I feel like the baker caught stealing from
the witch's garden, stealing for his wife, but that doesn't
matter because stealing is stealing and listening is listening. I know I'm in big trouble, because privacy is an
important thing, and the phone is not a toy.

I hang up fast and think, please, God, please don't let
Mrs. Coty call back and tell Mama someone was listening. Mama will know it was me and this nice day will be
wrecked because she'll be disappointed in me. Then I
won't be able to call Rosemary.

But the phone rings almost instantly, and I know it's
Mrs. Coty. So I let it ring. But Mama, who is downstairs
in the cellar doing the laundry, shouts, "Beverly, will you
please get that?" Now I have to pick it up. I think, OK, if
I apologize and promise never to listen again, maybe
Mrs. Coty won't tell on me.

I cross my fingers and lift up the phone.

"Hello?"

"Hello, Beverly?

It is not Mrs. Coty. It's Rosemary! Rosemary saying, "I miss you. Are you feeling better? When are you coming back to school?" It's Rosemary calling me, not just to say can you come over, but to talk, and I feel like a grownup standing in the kitchen talking on the phone. Rosemary's phone is on a small table by her front door, and I picture her sitting there, looking out into her living room or maybe looking up the stairs, her legs crossed like a secretary's.

We talk about arithmetic, jump rope and Leo MacNamara, and Mama doesn't tell me to get off the phone, because she's busy washing clothes. Mrs. Jablonski doesn't tell Rose to hang up either, and it's like being behind the bush at school. We talk about everything. I forget all about Mrs. Coty and about what I did until the phone clicks, and I hear someone on the line. Then I think, uh oh, she's picking up the phone to call my mother. So I say, very politely, "I have to hang up, Rose. Mrs. Coty, you can use the phone now," because I think, if I'm nice, Mrs. Coty won't tell on me.

I hang up, and a little while later Mama comes upstairs with the laundry.

"Did you talk to Rosemary?"

I nod.

"Are you feeling better?"

"Oh, I'm much better, Mama," I say, and I am because the phone doesn't ring, and Mrs. Coty doesn't tell.

The Guiding Light

There is a new priest at our church. His name is Father Finn. He has brown hair, and he walks fast, as if he is in a hurry to get where he's going. He's skinny, wears glasses and is serious but funny at the same time. And he is nothing like Father Kelleher, who has white hair and never smiles.

Father Finn came to the church hall the afternoon we were practicing flying up. He said he didn't know what flying up meant and made all the girls laugh. I said, "Hi, Father Finn," and he said "Hi, Beverly," and everyone except Janet Butler said, "You know him?" because he knows her, too.

I love Father Finn. I think he should be pope, and I told him this. I told him I'd vote for him, and he laughed. Sometimes now, after confession on Saturday afternoon, I'll ring the rectory doorbell and say, "Is Father Finn home?" The housekeeper will say, "Why don't you come in, and I'll get him for you," and I'll step into the dark, cool house where he lives with Father Kelleher and wait to see him.

He always acts surprised to see me, as if I have never visited before. "Well, what do you know. It's Beverly Curtin," he'll say. "And what can I do for you today?" I'll say, "Nothing, Father. I just want to say hi." Then he'll say, "Well isn't that just the nicest thing that's happened to me all day." And he'll ask me into the small parlor on the left because the big parlor on the right is Father Kelleher's and we're not allowed to go in there. He'll sit on his desk, not behind it, and I'll sit in a chair, and he'll ask me about school and my mother and father.

Then the phone will ring, or the housekeeper will come and say, "Father Finn, I hate to interrupt, but dinner's ready," or "The phone's for you," and I'll say goodbye and walk home.

Sometimes Janet Butler comes with me when I ring the rectory bell, but most times I go alone. Mama says, "Be careful you don't wear out your welcome, Beverly," but

I think Mama is wrong about wearing out your welcome. I visit Father Finn after confession, and I wait for him after Mass to say hi. I tell Rosemary all about him, because Rosemary is my best friend and I tell her everything.

I tell her about my mother's new favorite song, too. "Let Me Go, Lover." I like the song because it's fun to sing and because it makes my throat feel good. "Go-ho, go-ho, go-ho," I sing. And even when I'm not singing it, I'm thinking it in my head.

"I want to be a singer when I grow up," I tell Rose. She says that you don't want to be something, that you either are or you're not, and that I am a singer now, just one who hasn't made a record yet.

I teach her all the words to "Let Me Go, Lover," and we walk around the schoolyard singing it in our biggest voices. We don't stop even when Leo MacNamara and Stanley Burwell make fun of us.

I think Leo MacNamara is the most handsome boy in the whole entire school, but so does Rose. This means he can't be my boyfriend or hers. We have to share him, Rose says. So we decide to share Stanley Burwell, too, because he's nicer to us than Leo MacNamara. When I wait at the bus stop, Stanley always says hi to me, and Leo doesn't. Leo doesn't talk to girls. Rosemary says some boys are like that, that it takes most of them longer to mature than girls. I ask her how she knows this, and she says because she has a brother.

My mother has two brothers, Buddy and Billy, and my father has two brothers, Jimmy and Leroy, so there are a lot of boys in our family, but I never see them. My Uncle Buddy is handsome, not as handsome as my father, but more handsome than Leo MacNamara. He visited us once, but now he lives in California.

I don't know my Uncle Billy at all. He's just a picture in my grandmother's parlor. On her wall she has a giant painting of the pope, and on her TV next to a small picture of me in my First Communion dress, she has a big picture of Uncle Billy. "Where is he?" I asked Mama. "How come we never see him?"

"Because he lives in Virginia," she said. "And Virginia is a long way away."

My father's brother, Uncle Jimmy, lives in Rhode Island, which isn't that far away, but we don't see him, either. He used to be married to Laura, who my father said is beautiful, but I don't remember Laura, no matter how hard I try. Mama says I used to play with her daughter, Judy. I don't remember Judy, either. Jimmy has a new wife now, and I call her Aunt Fran.

We see my father's other brother, Leroy, sometimes. He lives near Little Nana and used to have a wife named Rita, but he doesn't anymore. She was tall and had dark hair and sad brown eyes. They had a daughter, Donna. Donna lives with just her father now.

Rosemary has lots of aunts, uncles and cousins, and they all visit each other on Sundays and holidays. The only aunt who visits me is Lorraine, and she doesn't visit very much anymore. She is in love, and Mama says love changes everything.

Peter Pan

*M*ama says, "Change into your pajamas, and then come right back downstairs."

Tonight is special. It's a school night, but I don't have to go to bed early. We are going to watch "Peter Pan," not a cartoon "Peter Pan," like we saw at the movies but a real "Peter Pan," with actors performing live all the way from New York. Mama says it doesn't matter that it's on way past my bedtime, because some things are more important than bedtime.

I run upstairs, take off my clothes, put on my pajamas and furry bathrobe, and race back downstairs to sit beside Mama on the big couch. She's wearing her bathrobe, too, only hers isn't furry. It's smooth and cool, and when I lean against her, her robe smells so much like the outdoors I wonder if she just took it off the clothes line.

My father comes around the corner. He's wearing a red flannel shirt and work pants. He never wears pajamas. I have never seen my father in pajamas in my whole life. "Only sissies wear pajamas," my father says. "Sshh, Larry. Don't say those things." But Mama smiles as she scolds him.

My father adjusts the TV. He's good at this. He fixes TVs in his spare time. He has a whole suitcase in our cellar full of tubes that look like light bulbs. Tonight he plays with the antenna until the picture stops jumping, then he plays with the knobs until the fuzz goes away.

"That's perfect, Larry," my mother says.

My father comes and sits beside me. He's on my left and my mother is on my right. Shane is stretched out on the floor.

When "Peter Pan" begins, my father starts making silly, high-pitched noises, the kind he makes when I'm watching "Gene Autry." My father thinks Gene Autry is a sissy, too — a sissy cowboy he calls him — and that makes me mad. He's a singing cowboy, that's all. I think my father must think that singing is like wearing pajamas, something men shouldn't do — except that he watches Perry Como and never makes fun of him. When Mama says "Sshh" this time, she is not smiling, and my father stops fooling right away. He sits up straight and turns and winks at me.

I love "Peter Pan." I loved the cartoon, but this is even better. Mama told me all about how the actors are playing the parts and how this Peter is really a woman dressed up as a boy. I know this, and at first I can even see this and the string that makes Peter fly. But then I forget; it's like Peter isn't an actor on a string at all, but a real boy flying and having fun. I wish I were Wendy so I could go with him, and take care of the little lost boys and be their mother forever.

I want Peter to sprinkle fairy dust on me. I want to fly out my bedroom window past the second star to the right. I'd ask Peter if we could take Rosemary, too. I don't have any brothers, and if Rose came the little lost boys would have two mothers to read to them, because Rose is an excellent reader.

I want to go to Never Never Land more than I have ever wanted anything, more than I want a brother or a sister even, because I don't ever want to grow up. I want to stay Rosemary's best friend forever. I don't want to get too old to play dolls and Monopoly. I want to eat grilled cheese sandwiches for dinner always. And I don't want to get all mushy over some boy.

I can think happy thoughts and I do believe in fairies. I know that if Peter tapped on my window tonight, I'd go with him, even though Mama would be sad and cry and miss me. I'd come back, though. I would. I'd come back and visit, and take her to Never Never Land, too. And even though my father thinks that boys who sing are sissies, maybe he'd want to go and help them fight Indians and fix their tree house. We could be so happy there. Maybe Mama could take home a little lost boy or a bunch of little lost boys. Then she wouldn't miss me so much, and she wouldn't be so sad that she didn't have a baby.

If only Peter Pan would come for me!

I say "No!" out loud to the TV when Wendy goes home and Peter flies away. Why is she doing this? But then he comes back, and I think, oh good. Wendy is getting another chance. This time I know she'll stay in Never Never Land.

Except it isn't Wendy in the bed in the nursery. It's a girl who looks just like Wendy and acts just like Wendy. Wendy is in the next room, a grown-up in a long, fancy nightgown.

I sob at the end of "Peter Pan," and my mother cries, too. My father pretends to be Tinkerbell. He sprinkles fairy dust on us and tries to make us laugh, but he can't.

My mother follows me up the stairs. She tucks me in bed. She kisses me good night. I wait until I hear her bedroom door close. Then I climb out of bed and open the window.

It's March and cold still, but I don't care. Just in case, I think. Just in case.

The Big Story

"God answered my prayers," I tell Rosemary.

"What do you mean?"

"I prayed just like you said. I said please, please, please one hundred times, and now my mother has a baby inside her."

"She does?"

I nod. We are walking to her house. We met halfway. That's what we do now because it's summer vacation. We call on the phone and say, "I'm leaving right this minute." Then we race out of our houses at the exact same time and hurry to the halfway place. Some days we walk to her house, some days we walk to mine, and some days we walk to the Dairy Queen or to the rectory to visit Father Finn.

We are walking to Rose's house now because Mama is resting. Having a baby makes you tired, my father said. I'm not supposed to tell anyone that Mama is having a baby. It's too soon, he told me, so it has to be our secret.

I don't tell anyone but Rose, and she doesn't count, because I tell her everything. Still, because this is such a big secret, I make her swear not to tell anyone else. I wish I could tell Janet Butler, Debbie Barnes and Father Finn. I wish I could tell everyone. I wonder if the baby will be a boy or a girl. I think I don't care, but I'm hoping for a girl anyway. I wonder what its name will be, and if it will look like me.

We play dolls at Rose's. I love to play dolls at her house because we pin all the clothes to the back of her couch and pretend that our dolls are shopping in a big department store. We have Toni dolls; they have lots of clothes but not the wedding gown. It costs a whole five dollars, more than our own dresses cost. My mother said that even if she could afford it, she would never spend five dollars for a doll's dress. But I think she would, if her ship came in.

When we get tired of playing dolls we go outside and play babies with balloons that we fill with water. The balloons break if you fill them too much or if you drop them. We pretend they are babies for a long time and even make little beds out of grass for them. But then we get sick of the game, so we say, "Abracadabra, you're not babies anymore. You're balloons," and we throw them at each other.

At the end of the day, my father drives me home. He comes straight from work, so he's wearing his police uniform and looks very handsome. I get in the car, and instead of driving to our house we stop at the Dairy Queen and get a coffee milk shake for my mother.

She is cooking dinner when we come in. Fried hamburger, corn and French fries, my favorite. I set the table without being asked. You can't tell that my mother has a baby growing inside her. She looks the same as she always looks, only tired. I don't understand how someone can sleep so much and still be tired.

My father and I do the dishes while my mother rests some more. Then I go upstairs, play my records and make a list of girls' names.

For Better or Worse

*L*ook at the picture. See how beautiful she is. See how he looks like Liberace.

It is July and hot. I am standing in my grandmother's kitchen, and there is no air, only heat like from coals. My dress — purple, nylon and see-through — is sticking to me. My hair is too short, my shoes are too tight and my socks have lace on the edge. I don't like this day, no matter how much everyone tells me I should.

"Don't you ruin this day," Mama said to me at home. "This is your aunt's wedding day, and it doesn't matter that you don't like Frank. She loves him."

My aunt is in the bedroom with my grandmother and mother, who are helping her with her veil. I am in the kitchen standing and waiting. Lorraine calls to me. "You can come in, Beverly. It's OK." But I don't want to.

This is my aunt's wedding day, and I know I should be happy because she's happy. Mama says that when you love someone you are always glad when they're happy. But I'm not glad. I'm sad because now Lorraine won't be just mine anymore.

My father is in the kitchen. He says, "Cheer up, honey. You're not losing an aunt. You're gaining an uncle."

Uncle Frank. I hadn't thought about this. The idea of Uncle Frank makes me feel worse.

I know that if I cry I will ruin the day. But I can't not cry. It's the worst day ever. It's hot, I'm wearing an ugly dress, and here comes Lorraine, walking through the door, looking exactly like Snow White with her dark hair, pale skin and pretty red lips, walking out the door and out of my life. Mama gives me a look that says, "Don't you dare cry." But it's too late. I am crying. I'm sobbing. But my Aunt Lorraine isn't mad. She kneels and pulls me close to her and hugs me.

"Sshhh," she says. "Sshhh. It's OK. I'm not dying, you know. I'm just getting married."

She smiles then, and I think how pretty she is and how selfish I am for wishing I could keep her all to myself.

"Come on, Baybo. Dry your tears and put on a happy face. Do it for me, OK?"

OK, I say. And I try. All day I try. And I guess I do a good job pretending to be happy because at the end of the day, on the way home, after the wedding and the big party, Mama turns to me and says, "I'm very proud of you. You behaved like such a big girl today."

I look at Mama and wonder why she doesn't know that I don't feel like a big girl, that I feel even littler than I did when I was small.

•   •   •   •

Mama says, "Do you think you would mind sleeping in the guest room for a while?"

"The guest room? You mean where Nana sleeps when she stays over?"

Mama nods.

I like the sound of the words "guest room." I like the room, too. It's way smaller than mine, but when you sleep upside down on the bed, you can feel a breeze in your face all night long. I sleep there on hot nights because in my room there's no breeze no matter how high I open the window.

I tiptoe across the tiny hall that separates my room from this other room, the guest room, and I lie upside down on the bed with my face to the window and my eyes closed. Some nights I pretend I'm Heidi sleeping in a hay loft in Switzerland breathing cool mountain air. Some nights I pretend I'm Wendy flying through the sky with Peter. It's easy to pretend when you're upside down with your eyes closed and sweet air cooling your cheeks.

I'd love to sleep in the guest room, I tell Mama. I don't mind at all.

"Well, that's good, Beverly," she says, "because your room is bigger, so that is where Lorraine and Frank should stay."

"Lorraine and Frank? They're gonna stay in my room? When? Tonight?"

I think how much fun it will be if they come and sleep over: how maybe Lorraine will bring chocolates, and we can sit on the couch and eat them; how I can stay up late; and how Mama will laugh out loud because Mama always laughs when Lorraine is around.

But then Mama says something that I don't understand. She says, "Just as soon as your father and Frank can get the room ready. Then they'll move in."

Ready? Ready for what?

"They're going to live here," Mama explains. "They're going to move in with us."

I think I must be asleep in the guest room right this minute, because this feels exactly like pretending. But no, it's real, Mama says. My father explains that he and Uncle Frank are going to start working on my room tomorrow. So I have to move all my clothes, dolls and toys into the guest room tonight. Mama helps me. When we finish, my father takes apart my bed and moves it and my bureau into the empty space at the end of the hall.

The next day Frank and my father polish the floor until it shines. Then Mama takes down the curtains and washes and irons them, and I iron the doilies because they're small.

It's a Sunday, and I am at the movies with Rosemary watching "The Glenn Miller Story" when Lorraine and Frank move in. I don't see them carrying all their things out of Frank's car into the house and up the stairs. I come home, and there they are.

My aunt and mother are in shorts sitting at the kitchen table, drinking coffee and smoking, though I don't know how they can, it's so hot. My father and Frank are having a beer.

I race upstairs to my room — I still think of it as my room even though it isn't anymore — and there are all my aunt's things: her red nail polish, lipstick, rouge, comb, hair pins, perfume.

The room smells like her, like Chanel No. 5. When

Aunt Lorraine told Frank it was her favorite perfume, he bought her a bottle. I breathe in the smell and decide that it's my favorite perfume, too.

Everyone is in the parlor now. Lorraine and Mama are sitting on the couch, and my father and Frank are sitting in chairs. I sit between my mother and aunt, and Lorraine says, "Oh, I almost forgot." She gets up, walks into the kitchen and returns with a box of Candy Cupboard chocolates.

We eat the whole box, except for the jellied chocolates, which no one likes, and then we eat dinner. Then the ice cream man comes and Frank says, "Who wants an ice cream?" Lorraine and I say, "We do!" So Frank gets me a Fudgicle and Aunt Lorraine a chocolate-covered.

Now it's eight o'clock, and I am so full and tired and happy that I don't want the night to end. The TV is on: I see its light through my closed eyes, and I hear Ed Sullivan's voice. I feel the warmth of my mother and aunt and hear them talking and laughing, my father breathing, Frank saying to Lorraine, "You OK, honey?" and Shane getting up and lying down, his collar rattling on the kitchen floor.

I feel my father lifting me, carrying me upstairs, tucking me into the guest room bed. I hear the bedroom door closing, footsteps going away, then footsteps coming back, the door opening and Lorraine's voice: "Good night, Baybo. Thanks for sharing your room with us. See you in the morning."

And I know this isn't pretend, that this is really true.

Aunt Lorraine and Frank

$\mathcal{D}o's$ and $\mathcal{D}on'ts$

he ice cream man comes twice a day, once at one o'clock and again at 6:30. "You could set your watch by him," Mama says.

I never, ever get two ice creams in one day. Sometimes I don't even get one. Sometimes Mama says, "No ice cream today, Beverly."

When I walk to Rose's, I see the ice cream man on Grove Street, and he always waves to me.

One day, when I have just a nickel for a Popsicle but I really want a Fudgicle, he gives me a Fudgicle anyway, even though it costs two cents more. He says, "What's two cents? Just don't tell, or everyone will expect a Fudgicle for five cents."

I think it must be fun to be an ice cream man. You get to drive all over town, eat all the ice cream you want and talk to kids all day. The ice cream man says it is a good job, and he likes it a lot.

Maybe I'll be an ice cream man when I grow up — a singing ice cream man. I could do that.

I'm buying two ice creams today: one for my aunt and one for me. Mama's at work, and Lorraine gave me the money for Popsicles. "I'll have two orange Popsicles," I say, and the ice cream man reaches into the middle section of his refrigerator chest and pulls them out. They are so cold and it's so hot out that they're steaming. "So you want to be a singing ice cream man?" he says. I nod and hand him my ten cents. "Well how'd you like to go for a practice run today?"

I say, "Really?" And he says, "Hey? Why not? After I get all these kids what they want, you hop on board, and I'll give you a ride to my next stop." There's a long line for ice cream so I have plenty of time to run home with Lorraine's ice cream. I bolt into the house, hand her her Popsicle, say, "I gotta go," and race back up the street before the ice cream man can change his mind.

"Perfect timing," he says. "All on board."

And I say, "Really? You're not kidding?"

"No, I'm not. Come on. Next stop Althea Road."

So I stand on the bottom stair and hang on to the door. He puts on the bell, and we're bumping our way up the street. All the kids, Janet, Ann Marie and Gregory Campbell, are saying, "Wow! That's not fair. How come she gets to ride on the ice cream truck?" And I am feeling so grown-up and special because no one in the whole neighborhood has ever ridden on the ice cream truck, not all summer, and here I am doing this wonderful thing.

We take the corner at Chestnut Street. All the kids are waving, and I'm waving, too, and the bell is jingling. I'm thinking I'm in a parade, and I'm feeling like the luckiest kid in the whole world.

But then all the kids stop yelling, and there's only one voice I hear. I recognize it instantly. It's my Aunt Lorraine's. I turn and look. There she is pumping her arms and speeding down the street, her white-heeled sandals flopping and she's screaming like I've never heard her scream. "STOP! STOP! YOU STOP THAT ICE CREAM TRUCK NOW! YOU STOP THAT TRUCK THIS INSTANT."

The ice cream man hits the brakes and stops so fast that I almost go flying. He stops so fast that he has to take his hand off the wheel to catch me because I'm about to fall out the door.

My Aunt Lorraine is beside me. She's yelling at the ice cream man. "WHAT ARE YOU DOING? WHERE DO YOU THINK YOU'RE GOING? WHERE DO YOU THINK YOU'RE TAKING HER?"

"He was just giving me a ride. He was just being nice."

"I'M NOT TALKING TO YOU RIGHT NOW, YOUNG LADY. I'M TALKING TO HIM. I'LL DEAL WITH YOU WHEN WE GET HOME. WHAT THE HELL IS WRONG WITH YOU?" she hollers at him.

The ice cream man is in trouble because of me. All he was doing was being nice, and here's Aunt Lorraine yelling at him as if he is some kidnapper. "I'm sorry," the ice cream man says over and over. "I didn't mean any harm. I was just giving her a ride." Lorraine drags me off the truck and tells the ice cream man, "IF YOU EVER DO A STUPID THING LIKE THIS AGAIN, I'M CALLING THE POLICE." Then she turns away from him and pulls me with one hand and hits me with the other all the way up the street.

"WHAT GOT INTO YOU? I CAN'T BELIEVE YOU TOOK OFF WITH A STRANGER. DON'T YOU KNOW ANY BETTER? DON'T YOU KNOW WHAT COULD HAVE HAPPENED?"

Even Gregory Campbell doesn't laugh when I walk by. All the kids are silent. All the kids look scared.

"Your mother would kill me if I let anything happen to you. Jesus, Mary and Joseph, Beverly, don't you know any better? Don't you know what could have happened?"

I know that the ice cream man will never like me again. I know that he wasn't doing anything bad, that he was doing something nice, but Aunt Lorraine won't listen. She says, "Don't you dare tell your mother about this. There's no use upsetting her. I just want you to promise me that you will never, ever do anything like that again."

"I promise," I say. But I still don't understand what I did wrong.

The Secret Storm

"It was a mistake," my father says before he goes to work. "Your mother's not having a baby." That's all he says.

Later, Mama is crying in the bedroom. I go to her door. "Mama? Mama?"

I open the door slowly, and she's lying there pretending she's asleep.

"Mama?" I say again.

"Go away, Beverly. Let me rest."

My father is at work, Aunt Lorraine is at Big Nana's, Frank is at sea, and Mama is crying. It's raining, the wind is blowing, and the house is dark and scary.

I want to tiptoe into Mama's room and lie down beside her because I am afraid of the rain and wind outside. But I don't because Mama said, "Go away," and I am trying to be good. So I go to my room and play Nurse Nancy, but it isn't as much fun as it used to be because I am older now, and I know my dolls aren't alive.

Elaine Maganello still thinks they are. She's a whole year older than I am, and she says that her doll cries and does real poops in her diaper. Elaine said she would show me the poops someday. But it won't be today. I look out my bedroom window, and I can hardly see her house it's raining so hard.

I wish I could call Rosemary and talk to her; I'm really scared up here in my room alone with the wind outside howling to get in. I wish I could call my father and tell him to come home. But the phone is next to Mama's bedroom, and I don't want to disturb her. That's what my father said this morning. "Don't disturb your mother, Beverly. Be very quiet today."

So I read instead. I read a story in my big Golden book about a boy with a drum who meets a princess on top of a glass mountain. They fall in love, but she can't leave the mountain because she's being held prisoner by a wicked old witch who makes the boy empty a lake with a thimble. I wonder if I could empty a lake with a thimble. I try to imagine it but can't because I don't know how deep lakes are. I only know that they're over my head and that I'm not supposed to go near them.

I fall asleep reading the story. I dream that I am the princess and that the boy has come to rescue me, but he can't find a thimble. When I wake it's nighttime dark, though it's the middle of the day. I turn on the light and walk downstairs.

"Mama?" I say out loud. "Mama?"

Now she is really sleeping, not pretend sleeping. I open the door the whole way, hoping she'll hear me, but she doesn't.

I sit at the kitchen table and watch the weeping willow trees in the back yard rock like a seesaw, and I think they're going to tip over because the wind is so strong. But they're trees, and trees don't tip, I tell myself. But I don't really know this. I don't know if the trees will tip over, if the house will fall down, if my father will be home soon, or if my mother will ever wake up.

So I sit at the table and wait because there is nothing else to do.

The trees do tip over, and the white trellis at the bottom of the front walk tips over, too, and flies down the street. There is so much rain that it has nowhere to go, so the street gets flooded. It's like a river running by.

My father is the one who discovers that the cellar is flooded. He opens the door, and we see the mattress that used to be on my crib float by. Everything that has been stored in the basement is ruined: my crib, my baby carriage, my high chair and baby clothes Mama was saving.

"It's a sign," my mother says. "I'll probably never need them anyway."

My mother sobs, and my father holds her.

He buys a pump, and the cellar is dry again. He drags away the weeping willow trees. Except for the holes in the back yard and the lack of a trellis out front, you wouldn't even know that there had been a storm.

Club Oasis

"Born on a mountain top in Tennessee, greenest state in the land of the free..."

"Robin Hood, Robin Hood, riding through the glen, Robin Hood, Robin Hood with his band of men..."

"Wyatt Earp, Wyatt Earp, brave, courageous, bold..."

Rosemary and I are arguing about who is better, Davy Crockett, Robin Hood or Wyatt Earp. I think Robin Hood is the best, but Rose says he's just a thief and that Wyatt Earp is the best.

I have a Davy Crockett hat, but I don't wear it to school. I only wear it when I watch "Davy Crockett" on TV. I wear my pistols, too, and my Annie Oakley vest, which is getting too small. I want to be a cowgirl when I grow up, but Rose says that there are no cowgirls anymore and that last month I wanted to be a singer.

I want to be a singing cowgirl, I tell her, like Annie Oakley. Rose says we should start a club because that would be more fun than always walking around the schoolyard singing songs. So we race over to the rocks at the edge of the playground where Leo and Stanley are digging in the dirt and decide. Rose decides, that the two flat rocks that look like a long bed will be our clubhouse. I say, "Why can't we have our clubhouse in our privacy place?" but Rose says, "No. This should be our clubhouse."

Rose says the next thing we need to do is to decide what kind of a club we're going to have. I say, "How about a flower club?" because when the lilacs are in bloom there's a whole wall of them on the other side of the yard; they smell so sweet that even inside you can smell them. And there are all kinds of other flowers we could learn about, like bachelor buttons and morning glories, that you grow from seed and that come in packages that you can buy at the five-and-ten.

I love the names of flowers and Rose does, too. We say "Petunia. Marigold. Daisy." We say the names out loud.

Rose decides that we need to make cards with the

names of all the flowers on one side and their pictures on the other. And after we do this, then we have to figure out who else we'll invite into our club. Rose says that she will be president, because she thought of the idea, and I can be vice president, if I want. The bell rings, and we go back inside.

The next day at recess, we run straight to our rock. Leo and Stanley are there sitting on it. "That's our club-house," Rose says, even though she still thinks Leo Mac-Namara is the cutest boy in the world. "You have to move," she tells him.

"What kind of a club do you have?" Leo asks, not budging.

"It's a flower club," I say, and the boys laugh so hard that they roll off the rock. "A flower club! What kind of a dumb idea is that? Who would ever want to belong to a flower club?"

Rose says, "It's not a real flower club. That's just a secret name because we don't want anyone to know what kind of a club it actually is because then everyone in the whole school would want to join."

Leo and Stanley stop laughing. Now they are curious. Now they want to know more.

So do I.

Rosemary kneels down. "Do you promise, do you swear on your mothers' lives that you won't tell anyone, if I tell you the truth."

They cross their hearts and hope to die.

Rosemary leans closer, and now her voice is just a whisper. "Are you sure you won't tell?"

They nod at the same time.

"It's, it's...I can't tell you," Rose declares.

"Whaddaya mean you can't tell us?" Stanley yells. "We swore on our mothers' lives."

Rose shrugs. "Maybe I'll tell you tomorrow."

"You tell, Beverly," Leo says, turning to me.

If I knew what Rosemary had in her head I'd tell,

because even though she thinks Leo MacNamara is the most handsome boy in the world — I think so, too — and even if she is president, and I'm only vice president, I'd tell what I knew. But I don't know what she's planning, so all I can do is shake my head.

The boys stomp away, kicking dirt, calling us babies.

Rose is bent over laughing.

"Wow! Did we trick them," she says, and I think "We?" She tricked them. She's the smart one. I just stood there saying nothing.

"We'll change it to the animal club. We'll draw pictures of scary animals, and then we'll invite the people who are most like those animals to belong. What do you think of that?"

I think Rosemary is so smart that she should get a triple promotion.

Rosemary Jablonski

Who Do You Trust?

*M*rs. Bouzan won't let me in her Girl Scout troop. She says there is no room for me. She doesn't tell Janet, Ann Marie, Michelle, Chickey Fleming or Mary Dolan, who is older, that there's no room for them. She just tells me. I knock on her door, and she opens it and says, "Sorry, Beverly. There's no room for you."

I don't understand. I flew up, I have my pin and I know my oath. I want to earn badges, march in parades and be a Girl Scout like everyone else. But Mrs. Bouzan says no. There is no room.

I watch all my friends walk to her house in their new uniforms, and I am inside in my new uniform with my pin on my collar with nowhere to go. Mama says she'll find a troop for me, but I don't want just any troop. I want to be with my friends.

Mrs. Jablonski calls Mama and says that she'll be a Girl Scout leader and that I can join her troop. I should be happy about this because Rosemary is my best friend. But I'm still sad. I don't understand why there isn't room for me at Mrs. Bouzan's.

"Why doesn't she seem to like me, Mama? What did I do wrong?"

Mama says I didn't do anything wrong and that it's not me Mrs. Bouzan doesn't like. She says Mrs. Bouzan doesn't like her. But that doesn't make sense because it's not Mama who wants to join Mrs. Bouzan's troop.

I go to Mrs. Jablonski's, and she's nice. I get to earn badges, sell cookies and learn how to rub two sticks together to start a fire so that we can toast marshmallows in the woods on outings. And in the spring I will get to march in a big parade next to Rose. But none of this makes me feel better. I feel left out. I feel like I stick out. All the kids in my neighborhood wear their Girl Scout uniforms to school on Tuesday, and I wear mine on Thursday. Everyone can look at me and see that I don't belong.

Aunt Lorraine says, "Forget about it, Beverly. If you look sad, that'll make that witch happy." That's what she calls Mrs. Bouzan, a witch. "Don't let that witch see that you're hurt. Pretend you don't care, and after a while you won't have to pretend, because you really won't care," she tells me.

I love Aunt Lorraine, and I think she is pretty, smart and practically perfect. But I think she's wrong about this. I know she's wrong, because I pretend and pretend, but I still care.

●　　●　　●　　●

In school this year, Rosemary sits at the front of the class. Sometimes when the phone rings in the principal's office, which is right across the hall from our room, Mrs. Cormey says, "Rosemary, would you please answer that."

Rosemary is so lucky. She gets to answer the phone, and she gets to be in charge when Mrs. Cormey, who is both the principal and our teacher, has to leave the room. I wonder if Mrs. Cormey would ask me to answer the phone if I sat up front instead of way in the back.

I practice talking like Rosemary. I practice saying my words the way she says them. I want to be just like Rosemary because she's pretty and smart; she has all the answers, nice straight hair, perfect teeth and skirts with blouses to match. Plus she gets to answer the phone.

I have mostly dresses with bows in the back, though I'm in the fourth grade now. My hair is short and curly, and my father is always telling me to take my fingers out of my mouth, or I'll get buckteeth. I think I have buck-teeth already, because when I look in the mirror I see the two front ones sticking out like Bugs Bunny's.

Mrs. Cormey gives us a paper that we are supposed to take home to our parents. It's a very important paper, she says, a permission slip so that we can get a polio shot. A doctor is going to come to our school and give everyone with a signed permission slip a shot so that we won't get polio. Mrs. Cormey is excited about this. She calls the polio shot "a miracle."

My mother says it's a miracle, too. I know about polio.

If you get it, you can't walk ever again, and sometimes you can't breathe unless you're in an iron lung. That's why Mama wouldn't let me swim in Houghton's Pond in the summer. She was afraid of polio. "Will we be able to swim in Houghton's Pond next summer?" I ask.

"We'll see," she says.

I don't want to get a shot. I get shots at the dentist's, and shots hurt. Dr. Conca says, "This won't hurt a bit," and then he sticks a needle in my mouth. I feel it going into my gums and coming out my eye. I scream because it does hurt, even though he says it won't.

One time Mama had to come into the room where I was sitting in the dentist chair and hold me on one side while a nurse held me on the other, so Dr. Conca could pull out a tooth. First, he stuck me with a needle. I screamed, and he said, "Sshhh." Then he said, "I promise, you won't feel a thing," but I felt him pulling my tooth; then I heard my tooth cracking. So I hollered, and Mama came running. Dr. Conca said, "Hold her down. Hold her down," and there was Mama holding me on one side and a big nurse holding me on the other and Dr. Conca pulling at me while I was screaming bloody murder.

Mama said on the way home that she had never heard such howling, and really, was all that necessary?

"It was, Mama. It hurt," I told her.

"Some things hurt, Beverly. And screaming doesn't make the hurt stop."

I promised I would try not to scream next time when the dentist lied and said it wouldn't hurt, then stuck me with a needle that killed. And I do try very hard not to scream. But I always fail. Sometimes I even cry on the way *to* the dentist.

What if I cry when I get my polio shot? What if I cry in front of all my friends? They'll think I'm a baby. They won't like me anymore.

Mama says, "Don't worry, Beverly. I'll take you to Dr.

Thompson to get your polio shot. You won't have to get it at school."

I am so, so lucky. I am going to get my shot in private. I am determined to be brave, not to cry, not even to look at the big needle the doctor is going to stick in my arm.

But when the doctor comes into the room, the needle is there in his hand, and though I squeeze my eyes shut so I can't see it, I still do.

"This is going to sting," Dr. Thompson says, and I like him because he doesn't say, "This won't hurt." I know this will hurt, so I get ready for it. I try real hard to be brave, but I can't help myself. I cry. I don't scream like when I'm at the dentist, but I cry, and I wish I could stop because I want to be brave and make Mama proud of me.

Mama says she's proud of me anyway. Mama says shots are scary things, especially when you're only eight years old.

At school I watch the kids wait in line for the doctor to give them shots. Some are very brave, but others scream and others cry. One girl throws up all over the floor, and the girl in front of her faints. At lunch when we're sitting on our rock, Rosemary says that the shot didn't hurt her at all and I say my shot didn't hurt me, either. I tell Rosemary almost everything, but I don't tell her that the shot did hurt and that I cried. I know she wouldn't like me as much if she knew I was a baby. Only Mama, who likes me no matter what I do, knows what a baby I am.

Grade 4 — Tower Hill School

The Mickey Mouse Club

Mama and Aunt Lorraine are sitting at the kitchen table talking about names. Mama doesn't like her name at all, because the only Dorothy she ever saw a movie about was Dorothy Gale, and that Dorothy was just a kid.

"I used to wait for one of the pretty girls with the long legs to be named Dorothy, but they were always Laura or Beth or Catherine," Mama says.

"Well, at least Ma didn't name you after a comb," Lorraine says back. Mama and Aunt Lorraine laugh about this, even though it's not funny being named after a comb. I wouldn't like it. I asked Mama a long time ago why she named me Beverly, and she said, "Because your father liked the name."

I wish my father had liked the name Debbie. Some of the boys call me Beverly Hills, and they laugh because they think they're so funny. But they're not. Leo MacNamara and Stanley Burwell never call me Beverly Hills. I wish I were Debbie, though, like Debbie Reynolds, or Darlene, like Darlene Gillespie on "The Mickey Mouse Club." She's my favorite Mouseketeer.

I watch "The Mickey Mouse Club" practically every day after school except on Thursdays when I go to Girl Scouts. Friday is my favorite show because it's "Talent Roundup Day" and ordinary kids can get to be "Honorary Mouseketeers." You can get to be an Honorary Mouseketeer if you can dance, juggle, play the drums or have a nice voice. Mama says I have a nice voice, but I don't think it's nice enough. But it should get better because once a week I take singing lessons from a lady who lives way past St. Bernadette's. Mama drives me there. She sits in one room while I stand and sing in another. I stand the whole time I'm there. First I sing the scale — but not like, "Do, re, mi, fa, sol, la, ti, do." I sing, "ah, ah, ah, ah, ah," and I have to sing big "ahs." When I finish I have to sing the "ahs" all over again, only this time with higher notes.

I am also learning a song called "The Bluebird of Happiness." "Be like I, hold your head up high, somewhere there's a bluebird of happiness."

"How come I can't learn songs like 'Let Me Go, Lover?' " I asked Mama. Mama said, "Because you already know that song." I should know "The Bluebird of Happiness," too, because I've been practicing it for weeks, but I don't. Mama says, "Have patience, Beverly. Rome wasn't built in a day."

I think that if I practice my singing and if I do a very good job, I might be on Talent Roundup Day, though I wouldn't want to sing "The Bluebird of Happiness." I don't know what I'd sing, but it wouldn't be that. I could dance, too, I suppose, because I go to dancing school at Mrs. Hedrick's house. But I think I'm a better singer than dancer because when all the kids move around the stage Mrs. Hedrick says for me to stand still. She says I'm the flower and they're the petals, that's why. But I think it's because I'm not as graceful as a petal should be.

"The Mickey Mouse Club" is over, so I wander back into the kitchen. Mama and Lorraine are still talking about girls' names, and I think this is strange because mostly they like to talk about real people, not just the names of people.

"How about Vera?" Mama says.

Lorraine groans.

"Norma?"

"No."

"Viola?"

They hold their stomachs and laugh so hard I think they might fall off their chairs. But they don't. They settle down and get serious again. I don't know how grown-ups can do this. When Rosemary and I, or Janet and I start laughing we can't stop until someone gets mad at us for laughing. Then we laugh even harder and don't stop until someone yells at us and makes us cry.

"What's your favorite girl's name?" Aunt Lorraine asks.

"Darlene," I tell her.

"Darlene? Darlene," she says in a voice that is like a question. Mama doesn't say a word, so the name just hangs in the air, like a note at the end of a song.

"Darlene," Lorraine says again. "Darlene Marie. What do you think, Dot? Do you like it? I think it has a nice ring to it."

"Why are you talking about names?" I ask Lorraine, and she looks at Mama, and Mama looks at me and says, "Because, Beverly, your aunt is going to have a baby."

"A baby? Aunt Lorraine's having a baby? I don't understand. Is it going to be our baby?"

"Well, the baby's going to live here with us upstairs so I guess it will sort of be ours for a while," Mama says.

A baby. Not Mama's, but Lorraine's. How come Lorraine's getting a baby and Mama isn't? I'm glad Lorraine's getting a baby, but I don't know why everyone gets babies but Mama. Mrs. Lyons has a new baby, Mrs. Barnes has a baby and Mrs. DiNatale, who lives around the block, has a baby. Babies are growing all over the place, so why can't Mama grow one?

I wish I could ask Mama this, or Aunt Lorraine, but I can't because you're not supposed to talk about these things. The way babies grow is a Big Secret that you can't know until you're older. I wish I were older so I could know now. If I knew the secret, then maybe I could help Mama figure out how to grow her own baby.

I look at Mama and wonder why she doesn't look sad that Aunt Lorraine's having a baby and she's not. I know I would be sad if Rosemary got to go on Talent Roundup Day and I didn't. I'd be sad and jealous, even though Rosemary is my best friend.

Mama tells Lorraine that she kind of likes the name Darlene Marie, too. They say it again. Together.

"It's decided then," Lorraine says. "If Frank likes it, and it's a girl, we'll name her Darlene. If it's a boy, of course we'll call him Frank Maurice Powers Jr."

I hope more than anything that the baby is a girl because one Frank in the house is more than enough. I don't even want to think about a little Liberace. I want a girl baby who looks just like Aunt Lorraine. I want a girl baby because I will have named her.

"When's the baby coming, Mama?"

"Not until after Christmas."

"Christmas is a long way away."

"Not that long, honey."

Lorraine buys a crib and a mattress, and Frank puts it together. There it is in my old room. Mama buys white sheets, a white blanket, diapers and booties. "We're having a baby," I tell Rose. She says, "Your mother's having a baby?" I say, "No. My aunt," and Rose says it's not my baby then.

But it is.

"It is, isn't it, Mama?"

"It's a little bit ours," Mama says.

Frank is at sea when the baby decides to come, so my father drives Aunt Lorraine to the hospital.

"Why are you going now in the middle of a snowstorm?" I ask my aunt. "Why don't you wait until it stops snowing."

"Because I can't wait," Lorraine says.

I can't wait either. We've been waiting way too long, so I understand about her not caring about the snow. Mama cares though. She's worried that Lorraine won't get to the hospital in time or that the car will get stuck somewhere along the way. My father says, "Don't worry, Dot. I put the chains on the tires. We'll be fine."

"Call me the minute you get there, Larry. Make sure you call."

I have to stay off the phone because Mama doesn't want my father to call and get a busy signal. I think it's lucky we don't have a party line anymore, or he would definitely get a busy signal.

I go upstairs and look at the crib sitting there waiting

for the baby, and I lie in my aunt's bed and fall asleep. When I wake up, Mama is sitting beside me crying.

"What's wrong, Mama?"

"Nothing's wrong. Everything's right. The baby's a girl — Darlene Marie Powers."

Darlene. I haven't even seen her, but I love her instantly. I think about all the nights I've wished on a star; all the birthday wishes I've made; all the what-goes-up-the-chimney, what-goes-down-the-chimney prayers; how many times I've asked Santa for a baby; the streams I've followed; and the pleases I've said.

I think about all the times I thought that maybe wishing is a waste. Now it's finally happened. There's a crib in my room. We have a baby. And in a few days, Lorraine will be bringing our baby home.

Darlene, Mama and me

The Fabulous Fifties

*O*h, it's the most wonderful time. Mama is singing, Lorraine is smiling, and Frank is at sea. My father is sitting and telling everyone who comes to visit how it was a very long ride from Randolph to Boston in the sleet and the snow with Lorraine sitting there, getting quieter by the moment — a most unusual thing for Lorraine, he always adds.

Darlene is the most beautiful baby. She has dark brown hair, big blue eyes and the softest skin. She smells like baby powder all the time, because Mama and Aunt Lorraine are always changing her, not just her diaper and her rubber pants, but all her clothes. Mama even irons Darlene's clothes, and she hates to iron.

I think Darlene likes me, because if I walk into her room when she's crying, she always stops and looks at me. I want to pick her up, hold her and rock her like Aunt Lorraine and Mama do, but they say, "No, no. You can't pick her up unless we're right there with you." They think I will drop her.

But I'd never drop Darlene. I know about the soft spot on a baby's head. If a baby is dropped on her soft spot, the baby's never right again. That's what Mama says. You can tell people who've been dropped on their soft spots. They get bigger, but they still drool like babies and they can't walk or talk. Sometimes if they're only dropped a little, like if they roll off a bed, they're OK. But sometimes, Mama says, they're not. They take spells, or they start to talk and forget what they're saying right in the middle of a sentence. "The world is full of people who have been dropped on their soft spots," Aunt Lorraine says, and Mama laughs.

I am very careful when I hold Darlene that I don't go near her soft spot because I don't want her to grow up drooling or forgetting. The one time I touched it, Mama made me. She put my hand in hers and guided it to the exact spot so I would know right where it was. I didn't like the feel of it. It was like touching a peach and coming to a too ripe spot. I pulled my hand away fast.

Now when I hold Darlene, when Mama and Aunt Lorraine let me, I tuck my hand behind her head and stay away from the soft part. Mama says that bone will grow over it in a few months, and when it does, then I can hold Darlene anytime.

Janet Butler comes over to look at Darlene, and she says Darlene is beautiful, too. This makes Aunt Lorraine happy. My mother's friend Vera, who lives next door, comes to see Darlene. She looks, nods, smiles and says to Lorraine, "You must be very proud," but she doesn't say Darlene is beautiful, and when Vera leaves, Lorraine says, "I don't like that woman."

Big Nana visits and says things like, "You're spoiling that child holding her too much," and "If you don't put her down and let her cry, she'll never learn how."

"Do babies have to learn to cry?" I ask Aunt Lorraine.

"Of course not," she says.

Every morning, before school, the first thing I do, even before I go to the bathroom, is peek in at Darlene. It's dark and cold, and Lorraine is asleep still, so I am very quiet. I tiptoe across the hall. I don't turn on the light because the light makes a click sound, and I don't want to make any noise. So I push open the door in the dark, creep into the room and look at Lorraine, her hair dark against the white pillow, her lips red even in the morning. Then I walk toward the crib, and I see her.

She sleeps on her stomach with her knees tucked under her, her face to the side. I think she must be dreaming of her bottle because her lips make a soft sucking sound. Her hands are tiny fists, and her fingers are the teeniest things. I wish I didn't have to go to school all day. I wish I could sit here in the dark and wait for her to wake up, then go downstairs, warm her bottle and feed her.

But I can't. So I fix her blanket, tiptoe out of the room, shut the door and go downstairs to the bathroom. Then I eat, get dressed, go to school and count the minutes until it's time to come home.

Rosemary says, "I don't understand why you have to go home every day. You never come to my house anymore."

Rose is right. I don't. I've even been skipping Girl Scouts. Mama says, "Don't desert all your friends, because when Lorraine and Frank move out, then what will you do?"

"When they move out? What do you mean, Mama? They're not moving out. They live here."

"They do now, but someday they'll get their own place."

"Someday? What day? Tomorrow? Next week? When will that be?"

Mama shrugs. "I don't know, Baybo. I don't know."

• • • •

Frank comes back from sea. He's knocking on the door one night, and Lorraine runs to answer it and there they are kissing and laughing. Then they go upstairs. Mama says, "Let them be. They need some time alone."

I don't mind having Uncle Frank here, really I don't. He still looks like Liberace, but he doesn't act like Liberace. He says to Mama and Lorraine, "Let her hold the baby. She's a big girl, now." He winks at me across the table when he sees me feed my broccoli to Shane. He doesn't tell on me.

On Valentine's Day, Uncle Frank comes home with the biggest red heart full of chocolates I have ever seen. It's so big that it covers almost half the kitchen table. It's so big that Lorraine says, "I don't think I can eat all of these," and she never says that.

Frank gives my mother a smaller red heart box of chocolates, then says, "Oops, I almost forgot," walks outside and comes back in again.

"This is for you," he says, handing me a pink satin heart with a pink rose on the top. I open it. It's full of dark chocolates, not just plain old candy hearts with "Dig me" and "Be mine" on them. I think, no one has ever given me chocolates for Valentine's Day before.

Frank kneels and whispers in my ear, "That's a little better than broccoli, don't you think?" I smile at him, and it's not a pretend smile this time; it's a real one.

We go into the parlor and eat our chocolates and watch "Name That Tune." My father is at work, but it's a nice night anyway because "Name That Tune" is fun, and the chocolates are delicious, and no one says, "Don't eat too many." Aunt Lorraine and Mama are on the couch, and I'm in the middle. Frank is sitting in the chair holding Darlene.

Uncle Frank and Darlene

The Green Pastures

I am in the garden by the back steps with my mother, planting bachelor buttons. I didn't start them in egg cartons like I did last year when I was in Brownies. They're just tiny seeds in my hand. I'm going to bury them, as they are, right in the ground. Mama says if I water them every day they will grow.

I am waiting for Mama to pull out all the weeds and dig the holes because I don't like to touch the dirt in the garden. There are worms in the dirt and worms give me the creeps.

"Chop off their heads and suck out their guts and throw their skin, away-ay-ay, long skinny slimy, fat gushy wushy, fuzzy, wuzzy wo-or-rms," Mama and I sing as she works. She says that someday I will like digging in a garden. She says that when she was young and lived in Haverhill she didn't like working in the garden, either. She hated the feel of dirt under her fingernails, and if she accidentally touched a worm, she'd scream as if it were a snake. But her mother made her do it. She had to plant lettuce, tomatoes, cucumbers and radishes, in addition to weeding and watering them. "I guess I'm spoiling you by doing the dirty work, huh?" Mama says.

Mrs. Tantillo thinks I'm spoiled. Ann Marie told me. Only children are always spoiled because their mothers buy them everything they want, Mrs. Tantillo said.

But my mother doesn't buy me everything I want. I want a bride's dress for my Toni doll and a small yellow stuffed bunny that's in the window of the drugstore. I want a square swimming pool with seats like Janet Butler has, and I want a brand new Raleigh bike with streamers on the handles like Rosemary's.

Ann Marie said that her mother's right, that I get practically everything I want. "Like when you want to go to the drive-in or Nantasket, your parents always take you," Ann Marie said.

I can't argue with Ann Marie about this because most times they do. They take me to movies, to the beach and to visit Sister Joseph Agnes in Chicopee. And they never make me do disgusting things like empty the garbage in the summer when there are maggots in the bucket, and they never make me dig in the dirt to plant seeds.

Darlene is outside in her carriage. A white net that keeps flies and mosquitoes away from her makes it hard for me to see if she's asleep or awake. I press my nose to the net and look at her, and her blue eyes are looking back at me.

Mama and Aunt Lorraine let me walk Darlene around the block every day. I love walking Darlene. Sometimes Janet Butler comes with me, and sometimes I go alone.

Mama shouts, "OK. It's time to plant the seeds."

I stop looking at Darlene, come back to Mama and put the seeds in the holes. Then she covers them with dirt. Then I say, "I think I'll walk Darlene now."

"Wash your hands first," Mama says.

I leave Mama watering as I strut down the street. I wonder if this is being spoiled, getting to go for a walk while your mother waters. But I don't think so. When we play at Rose's and get glue all over the kitchen table, her mother always cleans up.

Richie Maganello waves to me as I walk by. He's sitting on his front steps. He's Elaine Maganello's older brother, and he's very handsome. He has dark hair, brown eyes and the nicest smile. I wave back and feel my face turning red. I don't know why this happens. I like Richie Maganello, so why do I feel like I want to run away every time I see him?

Aunt Lorraine is painting her fingernails when I return. "Want me to paint yours?" she says.

I have short, ugly nails, not long, pretty ones like she has. But she says nails don't have to be long to be pretty; they just have to be well groomed. So Aunt Lorraine grooms mine.

Darlene makes gurgly baby sounds. Mama says, "Pretty soon she'll be talking." Lorraine says, "Pretty soon we'll be moving."

I don't want Aunt Lorraine to move; neither does Mama. But Lorraine says eventually she and Frank will have to get their own place.

"But not for a while," Mama says.

"Not for a long while," I beg.

Life With Father

I don't know how to ride a two-wheeler and everyone else does, but that's because everyone else has a two-wheeler and I don't. Mama says, "I don't want her on a bike, Larry. She could fall and kill herself."

My father says, "You have to let her grow up, Dot. She isn't a baby anymore."

"We can't afford a bike anyway, Larry. When we can afford one, then we'll talk about it."

Mama fell off a bike and broke her leg when she was twelve. That's why she's so afraid of bikes. That's what my father says.

"But I won't fall off," I tell him. "I'll be real careful."

"I know you will," he says. "She just worries about you."

Everyone has a bike except me. There's a great bike in the back of my Little Lulu comic books that I could earn just by selling 60 boxes of All Occasion Cards. All I have to do is fill out a form and say I want the bike, and I'll get the cards in the mail. After I sell them, they'll send me the bike.

I beg my father to let me do this, but he says, "No. Absolutely not."

"Why not, Dad?"

"Because I said."

Rose says I can ride her bike, but I say no thanks. I don't want her to know that I'm nine years old and that I don't even know how to ride a two-wheeler.

Every day I watch all the kids get on their bikes and ride down the street. They ride around the block, they even ride on Chestnut Street and some ride all the way down Old Street to the church. "Even if you had a bike I wouldn't let you ride on Chestnut Street," Mama says. "It's much too dangerous."

I am outside playing marbles in the driveway with Janet Butler when my father comes home and announces that he has a big surprise for me.

"You're so lucky," Janet says, even before she sees the surprise.

My father opens the car trunk and pulls out a bike, a green two-wheeler, not a Raleigh, not a lightweight bike like the one in the comic book, but an ugly looking thing with fat tires and thick handlebars.

"It's not new," my father says. "I know it's not exactly what you want, but the price was right. I even painted it for you."

I walk over to the bike, and I really don't like it. I think I hate it. But my father bought it for me, he painted it and he's going to get into an argument with Mama over it. Besides, an ugly bike is better than no bike at all.

So I lie to my father. "It's perfect," I tell him.

He hugs me, and I hug back. "OK, now for your first lesson," he says.

I don't want to get on that bike in front of Janet Butler, because she'll tell everyone that I'm a baby and don't know how to ride. But here's my father waiting for me, urging me on.

The bike is big, way too big for me. I can't sit on it and touch the ground. "I can't ride it, Dad."

"Maybe we can lower the seat," my father says. He walks inside to get his tools.

"It sure is different," says Janet. "At least you won't have any trouble finding it when it's parked with every-one else's."

"I like it," I tell her.

The seat can't be lowered. It's rusted underneath and stuck permanently in place. "It doesn't matter," my father tells me. "You don't need to be able to touch the ground to ride."

I wish I could touch the ground. It's hard to keep the bike steady while you try to get it going. But my father says, "Don't worry. I'll hold on to the seat until you get your balance."

At least Janet thinks I'm having trouble because the bike is so big, not because I'm a baby and don't even know how to ride. It's OK for my father to be helping me with this big bike. Even Janet would need her father to help her with a bike this size.

Mama comes out of the house and says, "Oh no, Larry. She's going to kill herself on that thing. Make her get off it now."

Aunt Lorraine says, "She'll be fine, Dot. Why don't you go check on the baby."

My father holds the seat, and I start to pedal. He starts to run and continues to run all the way down our street, saying, "That a-girl. That a-girl. Keep pedaling. Keep pedaling."

I am pedaling, and the bike is wobbling. My father is running and cheering me on. I take the turn to go around the block and I am pedaling harder, pedaling as fast as I can. My father says, "That a-girl. That a-girl. You've got it. You're doing it."

And I am. I've got it. I'm not wobbling. I'm riding a two-wheeler! I'm riding my own two-wheeler!

My father's voice is in the distance now. He's let go. I'm riding on my own. I'm riding all by myself. I want to look back and wave, but I can't because I have to concentrate on pedaling, not wobbling, steering and not falling.

I ride all the way around the block, past the DiNatales, the Bensons, the Bouzans, the Maganellos and the Montecalvos. I ride all the way without stopping and, when I get back to my own street, I am flying.

"Slow down," my father says. "Slow down." I slam on the brakes, skid to a stop and nearly fall off. I would have, but my father is there steadying the bike, steadying me.

"Great job," he says. "How'd it feel?"

"It felt great, Dad."

"Can I ride it," Janet asks.

"Can she, Dad?"

"It's your bike. That's up to you."

"Sure," I tell Janet. She gets on. My father holds the seat. She pedals, my father lets go, and Janet is off, flying around the block.

"So you really like the bike?" my father says. "I know it's a funny color. It wasn't supposed to come out that green."

"I really like the bike," I tell him. And this time I'm not lying.

My father and me

Dark of Night

I can't ride down Chestnut Street with all the rest of the kids. I can't ride my bike to Gilroy's because to get there you have to cross Chestnut Street. I can't ride my bike to Rosemary's because not only would I have to ride all the way up Chestnut Street, I'd have to ride on Lafayette Street, too, and that, Mama says, is totally out of the question.

"Please," I beg. "I'll be careful. I won't get hurt. I promise. All the kids can ride on Chestnut Street. Why can't I?"

"If all the kids decided to jump off the top of the Empire State Building, would you jump, too?"

My father says I have to do what Mama tells me, and Mama tells me the only place I can ride is around the block, so I don't ride all that much. It gets pretty boring going around in circles.

I go no-hands around the block when I ride. Mama never said, "Don't go no-hands, Beverly." So I ride around and around and take all the curves no-hands. I'm good at it. Janet says I go no-hands better than anyone she knows.

Aunt Lorraine and Uncle Frank have found a place to live. They're moving out soon. I can have my own room back, Lorraine says. But I don't want my room back. I want Lorraine, Frank and Darlene not to move and to live here forever.

"You can visit anytime," Lorraine says. "When school's out, you can come and stay for as long as you want. It'll be fun, I promise. I'm not going to the moon, you know. It's not the end of the world, Baybo."

But it feels like it is.

Rose says, "You knew she was going to move some-day. You knew she wasn't going to live with you forever."

It's Saturday, and we're up at Jean and Joan Betti's swinging on their swings. There are woods behind their house. Some days we cut right through the twins' yard to go exploring, but today we're just sitting and swinging.

It's a warm spring day. The Bettis aren't home, and we're glad because they have the best swings.

Rose pumps so hard and swings so high that I think she is going to fly right over the top. I picture her, her eyes wide, her hair out straight like cartoon hair, her mouth open but silent — Rose would never scream — flying through the sky, then landing on the ground with a terrible thud. "Be careful," I tell her. "You're going too high."

"No, I'm not," she says and pumps harder.

Rose is my best friend, and she knows everything about me, but she doesn't know how scared I get sometimes about her falling off a swing, dying and leaving me, and about Lorraine and Darlene leaving me, too.

We play on the seesaw for a while. Then we walk down to see Father Finn. I tell him about Darlene, and he says, "You must be very sad."

I am sad, and even seeing Father Finn doesn't help.

A few days later I come home from school, and Frank, Lorraine and Darlene are in the kitchen with my mother and father, dressed as if they're going somewhere.

"We didn't want to leave without seeing you," Lorraine says.

"You're going now? You're moving today?"

Lorraine nods. "Our stuff's in the car." She writes her new phone number on a piece of paper. She says, "I left you some nail polish and a nail brush. They're on your bureau." She opens her arms and hugs me.

We kiss goodbye. We walk out to the car. We stand on the street, my mother, father and I, and watch Frank open the door for Lorraine. Lorraine gets in, smooths her skirt and positions Darlene on her lap. Frank gets behind the wheel, turns the key and drives away.

They wave. We wave.

And then they are gone.

Stars on Parade

*M*ama saves change in a jar, which she keeps in the back of a cabinet where my father never looks. She won't touch that change, not even when she's out of cigarettes or when I beg for a dime for a Little Lulu comic book. That's her anniversary money, she says. She's saving up to buy a present for my father.

It's their tenth anniversary coming up in August. Mama says she's going to make a record, a real record at a real recording studio in Boston. She says she's made an appointment and that she'll sing "Mr. Wonderful," because my father is Mr. Wonderful. She wants me to sing, too. "You can pick any song you like," she tells me.

So I choose, "Let Me Go, Lover."

I skip school the day we make the recording. My father gets up, leaves for work and says, "See you two later." Mama and I exchange smiles because my father thinks it's an ordinary day. But it isn't ordinary at all.

We walk down Chestnut Street to the bus stop, take the bus to the train station and take the train to Park Street. Then we follow the directions that a man gave Mama on the phone.

The building is somewhere we've never been on a narrow street far from the train station. It's a damp day, gray and cold, and my feet hurt because I have my patent leather shoes on. I look at Mama's feet — she's wearing high heels — and I think her feet must hurt even more.

But Mama isn't worried about her feet. She's worried about the song. She wanted a piano player to accompany her, but that costs ten extra dollars, so she's going to sing alone. "I hope I don't make a mistake. I hope I do a good job," she says.

"You will, Mama," I say, taking her hand.

We find the address, open the door and walk up some very steep steps. Then there's another door. We open it and everything's glass. There's a fat man in a glass booth surrounded by knobs and buttons. He sees us, but he doesn't wave or smile. So we sit on some wooden chairs.

It feels good to sit. We watch the man in the booth, but he doesn't look at us. Then a skinny man appears. He says to Mama, "Mrs. Curtin? Come with me."

Mama hands me her coat and pocketbook. The man in the glass booth looks up, puts on headphones, and lights a cigarette. I watch Mama walk to the middle of the room, where the skinny man leaves her under a microphone that hangs from the ceiling. I can tell that my mother is nervous because she plays with the red beads around her neck, pats her skirt and shuffles from foot to foot.

The man in the glass booth yells, "You're going to have to stand still if you want this to work."

Mama stands still as a rock. A red light comes on, the fat man nods, and she sings. "Why this feeling, why this glow, why the thrill when you say hello? It's a strange and tender magic you do. Mr. Wonderful, that's you."

Her voice fills the room, and it's perfect, just as it always is. She doesn't need a piano player.

The man in the glass booth is staring at my mother, not ignoring her anymore. He's not puffing on his cigarette. It's as if he's forgotten he's smoking it.

That's just what Mama's voice does. It makes you forget things.

There is more space on the record. "Sing another song," the man in the glass booth says. So Mama sings, "Oh, we ain't got a barrel of money, maybe we're ragged and funny. But we'll travel along, singin' a song, side by side." And at the end, when the song is finished, she pauses and says, "Happy anniversary, Larry," and the man in the glass booth smiles.

Then it's my turn. I sing "Let Me Go, Lover" and "Have Faith, Hope and Charity." Mama says I did a great job, but I know I didn't. She should have sung on both sides. But she says, "No, Beverly. One side's enough. This is a present from both of us."

The skinny man wraps the record in paper, Mama pays him, and we head on home.

Beverly Beckham

Mama

See It Now

*I*t's summer and hot all the time, hot everywhere — outdoors and indoors — and hottest in the car, even with all the windows down. It's cool only in the cellar where I like to hide. But Mama says, "I don't want you in the cellar. Go outside, Beverly. The fresh air is good for you."

In the cellar, I read comic books, suck on fireballs and drink water with ice cubes in it. Outside, I sit on the steps and wish I were inside, or I chase butterflies and trap them in a jar, or I take off my shirt and run in my shorts under the sprinkler.

Some days I meet Rose up at Tower Hill School. We play on the swings or make gimp bracelets with the rest of the kids who go there every day. When we get tired of making bracelets, we walk to her house and play dolls. We are wallpapering an old chicken coop that her father built so we can have a real doll hospital. The wallpaper doesn't match but, because we're using scraps left over from houses her father built, that's OK. The chicken coop looks better with wallpaper that doesn't match than with no wallpaper at all.

One week we go to Girl Scout camp. It's not a real camp where you sleep over at night, it's only a day camp, but it's fun. We toast marshmallows in the woods around a real campfire, which we make ourselves. After we eat all the marshmallows, we sit around the fire and sing songs.

Every night after supper, Michelle, Ann Marie, Janet, Judy Bouzan and Chickey Fleming play tag, Red Rover or One-Two-Three Red Light. We play until the street lights come on and our mothers call us in. Sometimes Janet gets to stay at my house after dark, and we sit on my front steps and make up stories. Sometimes I tell Janet the stories that Little Nana has told me and sometimes I make up my own.

I like it when Janet tells stories. Hers are always about poor little girls lost in the woods who run into witches, giants and dragons, but who are always saved by a hand-some and rich prince disguised as a poor farm boy or a frog. I love Janet's stories almost as much as I love my grandmother's. I forget when I'm listening to them that the mosquitoes are biting, that Darlene is gone, and that I don't really like playing with Judy Bouzan at all, because I think her mother is mean. Janet's stories make all these things go away.

When my mother shouts, "It's time to come in Beverly. It's time for bed," I never want to go. I wish I could listen to Janet's stories all night long. Sometimes my father takes me places at night. If I say, "Please, Dad, can we go to the drive-in?" he'll always say yes. Mama loves going to the drive-in, too, so she'll stop what she's doing to come along. Her favorite movie so far this year is "The Girl in the Red Velvet Swing." She hasn't stopped talking about it. It's a true story, she's told me at least a million times. "I know, Mama, I know." I liked "The Girl in the Red Velvet Swing" a lot, but I love horror movies. Last year we saw "The Naked Jungle," and I still think about all those ants eating people, and how, if you fell down when you were running away from them, they ate you in seconds.

If I tell my father I'd really like to go to Dairy Queen, he'll say OK to that, too. "Let's hop in the car," he'll yell, and off we'll go, Janet, if she's still here, and Mama, too. Mama loves strawberry sundaes almost as much as she likes orange-filled chocolates and "The Girl in the Red Velvet Swing."

If I beg my father to go to Nantasket Beach to the amusement park, he won't always say yes because Nantasket is a long drive. But sometimes he'll say, "Go get a sweater," and he'll ask Mama if she wants to come along but she always says no because she doesn't like amusement parks. "You two go and have a good time," she says.

My favorite thing to do at Nantasket is to ride the rocket ships. We go round and round; they're fast, and

I'm up high, but I'm not scared way up there in the sky because I'm with my father. I know the cables won't break and the rocket won't crash — though Rose says things like this happen all the time. My father knows a lot of policemen at Nantasket because he works with them. Sometimes they give us free passes; and then we can ride everything, the scrambler, the bumper cars, the caterpillar, even the Tunnel of Love. But I like the rocket ships the best.

My father tries to win me things. He'll stop in front of a big display of stuffed dogs and say, "Pick a number, Beverly." Then he'll put a nickel down on that number, a wheel will turn, and my number will roll by. The wheel never stops on it. I tell my father, "I don't need a stuffed dog. I have a real dog." But my father thinks I'm saying this to make him feel better.

Rosemary's mother wins candy at the Brockton Fair every year from Kelly the Candyman. She wins piles of it, boxes and boxes she gives to people because she has so much she can't eat it all. She's excellent at guessing numbers. I'm not, and neither is my father.

Before we leave Nantasket we always buy my mother a box of salt-water taffy and a package of dulse. I love salt-water taffy, especially the molasses ones, so I open the package, search for these and eat them all the way home. But I never eat the dulse. Dulse is dried seaweed, and it's disgusting. I can't believe my mother likes stuff that washes up on the beach.

I've been to visit Lorraine once this summer, and she says I can go back anytime. She lives on Chalk Street in Cambridge, which is near where we used to live and is a long way away. She has a little apartment with just one bedroom. I slept on the couch in the parlor under a cuckoo clock. Frank bought her the clock. It's wood with big gold chains hanging down and a cute little bird that comes out of its house and cuckoos every hour.

I loved lying there in the dark listening to the clock

tick-tocking, to Darlene making her squeaky sleep sounds and to Lorraine and Frank breathing.

Every morning Lorraine made me French toast because I love French toast. Then we'd get Darlene dressed and take her for a walk. We walked to a toy store the first day and, even though Lorraine said, "Pick out something; I'll buy it for you," I couldn't. I know Aunt Lorraine doesn't have money to be wasting on toys. So I said what Mama taught me to say, "No thank you, Aunt Lorraine. I don't want anything."

I stayed at her house for almost a week, and we walked Darlene every day. I helped Lorraine dust, fold towels and set the table. One day, after we finished all our chores, we went to see Big Nana at the Shamrock Cafe, then stopped in Central Square before we went home.

The flower man almost didn't recognize me. "Look at you. You're such a big girl, all grown up now," he said. "And look at this one, such a little doll," he said to Darlene. He gave us flowers, even Darlene, who tried to eat hers.

The morning I was to go home, I woke up, and Aunt Lorraine wasn't there. Uncle Frank was in the kitchen with Darlene, who was dressed and fed. Frank said, "Well, good morning, lazy bones. I was beginning to think you were never going to wake up."

I didn't want to wake up and get up and go home.

"Where's Aunt Lorraine?" I asked.

Frank smiled and said, "She's gone to get you a surprise."

I thought the surprise was donuts, because I love donuts. This was my last morning at her house, so that's what I expected. But when Lorraine walked up the stairs, she wasn't carrying a donut bag. She was carrying a big, rectangular box.

"Surprise!" she said, handing it to me. Lorraine had walked to the toy store and bought me an art kit — not a little kids' one, but a real art kit with different size paint brushes, tracing paper and books that all you have to do is wet them and a picture appears. Plus a big wooden box to keep everything in!

"I thought you'd like it," she said. "I thought it would give you something to do when you got feeling a little lonely at home. Is it OK?"

I knew Lorraine couldn't afford this. I knew I should have said, "It's very nice of you, Aunt Lorraine. But I don't need it. I have lots of paints and brushes at home."

But I couldn't lie. I loved the art kit. But most of all, I loved my Aunt Lorraine for knowing that I would.

The Flying Wallendas

*R*ose calls me on the phone. "Hello, Bev. This is Rose," she says, as if I don't know who it is. As if anyone else ever calls me. "You know how we were playing on the swing this afternoon? You know how high we went?"

I know. Rose doesn't have to remind me. Rose has a big wooden swing her father hung between two trees and her favorite thing is to swing and swing and go as high as she can. Then she jumps off and lands in the tall grass that's part of the big field in her yard. I watch her do this all the time, and she says, "Come on. You do it. You try."

But I don't.

This afternoon we were sitting on the swing together talking and singing, and I wasn't noticing that we were swinging until we were really swinging. "Stop pumping," I told Rose. "I don't want to go any higher."

"Then get off the swing," she said, pumping harder.

The only way to get off the swing was to jump. I didn't want to jump because jumping is just like falling, only you know it's going to happen.

"Stop pumping," I said again.

Rose pumped harder, and we went higher — higher than I've ever gone — and I hated it. But I didn't jump, I just hung on. Then Rose jumped, I stopped pumping, the swing stopped and I walked home.

"After you left, I stayed on the swing and kept practicing my jumps. Every time, I went a little higher, until the bar way up on the top of the tree came loose."

"That big metal bar came loose?"

"It did," said Rose.

"Where were you?"

"In the middle of a jump, or the bar would have hit me on the head and I'd be dead. That's what my father said. I'm glad you went home when you did. You might have been hit on the head."

I don't tell Mama this. I don't want her to know that the metal bar that Mr. Jablonski hung between two big trees came flying down and almost killed his daughter and could have killed his daughter's best friend. If she knew this, she wouldn't let me play at Rosemary's anymore.

Mama worries about me too much. That's why she won't let me ride my bike with all the kids, or go ice skating on the pond in the winter, or go sledding down the big hill across Chestnut Street. Little Nana told me it's only natural for Mama to want to protect me because I'm her only one. "God knows what would happen to your mother if anything happened to you," she said.

• • • •

I am riding my bike around the block no-hands because there's nothing else to do. It is August, and Rose is school shopping in Quincy with her mother, Janet is inside watching TV, and Ann Marie has gone to the cottage with her family. Michelle, who is only going into fourth grade and someone I hardly play with anyway, has gone with them. Mama says I have to play outside, but there's no one to play with and nothing to do.

I am riding my bike no-hands around the block with just my red shorts on because it is a very hot day. Janet told me that her mother says that girls our age are supposed to wear tops all the time, even when it's very hot, but Mama says, "You're only nine. You don't have to wear a top."

So I'm riding around no-hands, with no top on, watching my chest shake because it does a little. It's not as flat as it used to be, and I'm just noticing this. I'm thinking that maybe Mrs. Butler is right. Maybe I should have a top on because my own top is definitely jiggling. I'm thinking, I don't like this, and I hope Richie Maganello isn't outside because I'm going home right now to put on a top. I'm certain he's not going to be outside. I've been around the block twice already, and I haven't seen him. I don't even think he's home.

Most times, I love to see him. I love to fly past no-hands, not even glancing at him but seeing him anyway.

But not now, not when I feel my chest shaking and sticking out all white and bouncy, not when I'm wondering when did *this* happen? Not when I'm wishing I had never come outside in just my red shorts.

But, oh no, there he is. And not just Richie, but his older brother too, plus the two boys from across the street. The four of them are standing on the front steps talking, and I think they won't notice me. They're busy. I'll just keep pedaling, keep flying. I'll be past them in a jiffy, and I'll be home in my bedroom putting on a shirt.

Except that, I don't know, because I'm jiggling, because I'm nervous, because I'm holding my breath and pedaling as fast as I can, because I'm not paying attention, because I'm thinking of Richie Maganello looking at my chest, I tilt. I'm going a million miles an hour, no-hands, and I tilt. I lose my balance and grab the handlebars, but it's too late. I'm flying over the handlebars. I'm flying through the air, and here comes the ground, tar and pebbles and sand. I hit it with my palms and knees and skid to a stop.

I don't cry. I want to. My palms and knees are on fire, worse than the dentist's drill. But far worse is that I'm lying there on the ground, in the dirt, in front of the Maganellos with no top on.

Richie, his brother and their two friends come running. They're yelling, "Are you all right? Are you all right?" And I yell back, "I'm fine, really," like the brave little girl I am not. If only Rose could see me now pretending that I haven't just sailed though the air, a thing I've gone out of the way not to do. But at least I'm not crying. At least all they can see, as long as I get up and walk away, is my bare back. And at least I live just three houses away.

I walk into the house, and Mama looks at me and says, "Oh, my God, what happened to you?" She runs and gets soap, a cloth, Mercurochrome and Band-Aids and washes my cuts. Shane comes and licks me. I cry then because I'm home, alone and safe.

"It's my fault," Mama says. "I should have let you stay inside. If I had let you watch TV, like you wanted, this wouldn't have happened. It was too hot for you to be riding around on that bike. Did you get dizzy and lose your balance?"

"I don't know what happened," I tell my mother. And I really don't. I don't tell her I was going no-hands because that wasn't the reason I fell. I don't tell her about my bouncy chest because this would make her feel worse.

Mama gives me two dimes and a nickel and says I can buy two comic books and a Popsicle and sit in the cellar and read for the rest of the afternoon if I want.

I take the money then walk upstairs and put on my red-and-white-checked halter top before I walk to the store with Shane.

Teacher's Pet

*R*ose is wearing a skirt and blouse on the first day of fifth grade. I have to wear a dress. Mama says I look nice in dresses, but I don't agree. I think I look like a baby.

We buy my dresses at Conrad and Chandler. We drive to Forest Hills. Then we take the train to Boston, school shop, light a candle at Arch Street and eat macaroni and cheese at Colestone's. The macaroni and cheese is my favorite part.

It's not that I hate the dresses I have to wear, they're pretty. One's red plaid, one's shiny pink, and one's light blue. They all have great wide skirts so I can wear my crinolines under them. I just wish sometimes that I could look like everyone else. Mama says, "Why would you wish that? You're you. You should be proud of who you are."

We're going to Tower Hill Annex this year because there are so many fifth-graders that there's not enough room for all of us at Tower Hill School. The Annex is a big white building that looks like a barn and it is right across the street from Rosemary's house. She could practically roll out of bed and be in the schoolyard. This means she can watch TV in the morning until she hears the school bell.

I hope Rose and I are in the same room. There are going to be two fifth-grade classes this year, not just one. Mr. Holmes is going to teach one class, and Miss Nagel is going to teach the other. I keep my fingers crossed all the way to school hoping that I get Miss Nagel *and* Rose, but I don't. Mr. Holmes calls out his students' names, and right at the beginning he shouts, "Rosemary Jablonski." Rose looks at me and crosses her fingers, and I think maybe having Mr. Holmes wouldn't be so bad after all. I don't care who I have, as long as I'm with Rose.

But my name isn't called, and I feel sad and a little scared as Rose files into her classroom without me.

Miss Nagel's class is everyone who's left. I look around

and see Janet Butler; Chickey Fleming; Stanley Burwell; and Bobby Fletcher, who, I think, likes me; Johnny Nelson, who looks like Elvis Presley with his slicked-back hair; and George Falcone, who is even cuter than Leo MacNamara.

Miss Nagel has the upstairs classroom, and Mr. Holmes has the downstairs one. I see Rosemary in her seat as we file by. I wave, and she waves back. Janet says, "We're so lucky we got Miss Nagel."

It's hot upstairs even though all the windows are open. I wish I hadn't worn so many crinolines under my plaid dress. Miss Nagel has the desks arranged so that they form a big square. She says we can sit anywhere we want, so Janet and I sit next to each other.

There are two posters on the bulletin board, one of Adlai Stevenson and one of President Eisenhower. This is an election year, so everyone is talking about who's going to win. To tell if it's an election year, you divide the year by four, and if there's no remainder, then you know it's time to vote. Mrs. Cormey taught us this last year in long division. Janet's parents are going to vote for Adlai Stevenson, so she wants him to win. My parents are going to vote for President Eisenhower, because he used to be General Eisenhower, so I want him to win.

Miss Nagel is so pretty, even prettier than when we were in second grade. She wears snappy shoes — that's what my mother says. She wears high heels, fancy dresses and bright red lipstick. She's nice, too. She says that she's happy to have many of her old students once again, and she looks at Janet and me when she says this. She says fifth grade is a very important year; we have lots of work to do and lots of material to cover, and we're going to have to work very hard. "I know it's difficult to be in this makeshift classroom," she says, looking around, "but we're just going to have to dig in and work as hard as we can and ignore our surroundings."

I don't know what makeshift means, but I like our surroundings. It's hot and stuffy, but I like the desks in a big square, all the open windows, the trees outside and Janet sitting beside me. Miss Nagel says that she needs our cooperation and that she knows we'll give it to her because we're good boys and girls. And we nod because we know Miss Nagel, and we love her.

She passes out our books, and we write our names in them. She says, "Don't forget to take them home and cover them tonight." Then she passes out composition books, which she says will be for the writing we do, and we put our names on these, too. Then she gives us red construction paper cut in thirds.

"I bet you're wondering what these are for," she says, and we nod and say, "Yes, Miss Nagel."

"These are your conduct cards," she explains. "These cards will determine what grade you get in conduct."

Sometimes I get C's in conduct. Mama yells at me, storms up to the school and says, "Tell me what awful things my daughter has done to deserve a 'C' in conduct." The teachers always tell her the same thing: I talk too much. I don't mean to talk too much, and I don't think I talk more than anyone else, it's just that I always get caught talking. Miss Nagel says that people who talk while someone else is talking, talk without raising a hand, or talk when no talking is allowed will get a punch on their conduct card. She demonstrates what a punch is by taking a paper puncher and making a hole in one of the cards. People who get no punches will get an 'A' in conduct. People who have many punches will get a corresponding grade.

I don't know what corresponding grade means, but I understand what Miss Nagel means. No talking. I whisper to Janet, "This is going to be hard."

Miss Nagel says, "Because it is so hot up here, I suggest we move the classroom outdoors. Children, please take a pencil and your composition books and file out. There will be no talking or pushing. Follow me, please."

We follow Miss Nagel down the iron fire escape so that we don't disturb Mr. Holmes' class. I start to sing, "We're following the leader, the leader, the leader. We're following the leader wherever he may be," which is a song from "Peter Pan" and which just spills out of me through no fault of my own.

"Beverly Curtin! Did you hear me say there would be no talking?"

"I wasn't talking, Miss Nagel. I was singing."

"There will be no singing, either," Miss Nagel says.

It's lovely sitting outside under the big trees listening to Miss Nagel read us a story. She says that in order to learn how to write well you have to first learn how to listen. So we sit and listen as she reads a story about a beautiful Hawaiian girl who wants to learn how to fish.

When Miss Nagel finishes the story, she tells us to write how we feel about it in our composition books. Johnny Nelson says, "I forgot my pencil. Can I go back upstairs and get one?" Miss Nagel says, "MAY I go upstairs?" and then says, "That won't be necessary, John," and pulls a brand new, just-sharpened pencil out of her book bag.

After we write our compositions, we go back inside and find Hawaii on the map of the world. Then it's time for recess, and we go back outside again. Rose says that she's spent the morning learning about atoms. Mr. Holmes stood on a chair and pretended to be an atom. He made all the girls electrons and all the boys neutrons. I don't know what an atom is, really, except I know that all things are made of atoms — desks, books and even people — but you can't see them unless you look under a microscope. Rose says that Mr. Holmes has his own microscope, which he is going to bring into class someday.

At lunch time, Miss Nagel lets us talk at our seats. Bobby Fletcher starts to talk to me, but I don't want to talk to him. I want to talk to Janet. But she's talking to

Chickey Fleming, so I have to talk to Bobby. I'm glad when it's time to go outside again.

After school, I don't take the bus home. I walk to Rose's, and we have milk and cake from the bakery truck that comes to her house twice a week. We play marbles in her driveway, then go inside and look through the newest *Modern Screen* magazine for stories about Debbie Reynolds and Eddie Fisher. Rose and I have Debbie Reynolds and Eddie Fisher scrapbooks. We cut out pictures from magazines and paste them in these books. Rose has more pictures than I do because her scrapbook really is for Debbie Reynolds *and* Eddie Fisher. I don't like Eddie Fisher, so I cut him out of my pictures.

My father picks me up and drives me home. Mama's in the kitchen frosting cupcakes. She works at Whitey's Bakery in Weymouth now, and they taught her how to make flowers out of frosting. In the center of every cupcake, she's made a pink rose with green petals around it. I can't draw a rose with a crayon. I can hardly trace a rose even with the art kit that Aunt Lorraine gave me. "What do you think?" Mama says. "I'm still having a little trouble with the petals. But I thought I'd make them to celebrate your first day of school."

I think the petals are perfect. I think this whole day has been perfect. I think I'm going to love fifth grade.

Your Hit Parade

"Thee I love, more than the meadows so green and still, more than the mulberries on the hill, more than the buds on the May apple tree, I love thee."

This is the new song I'm learning in singing. I have to stand when I sing. I have to open my mouth wide and breathe properly, and I have to be attentive to my phrases.

I don't want to be attentive to my phrases, and I don't want to take singing lessons anymore. But Mama says once you start a thing you should always see it through. If I still don't want to take singing after my recital, she says, then I can quit. But not before.

I wish I could sing, "Yoo-hoo, my honey, yoo-hoo, my honey, gonna get along without you now." Or I wish I could sing "Wanted," because that's my new favorite song. But no. My singing teacher says I have to sing "Thee I Love" and "The Bluebird of Happiness" at my recital, because these songs showcase my range.

I don't want to showcase my range. And I don't want to sing at a recital. The recital is not for two more months, so I try not to let it wreck my life. Rose says I'm being ridiculous, that she likes "The Bluebird of Happiness." When she sings it, I like it, too. I wish I had Rosemary's voice. I think she sounds just like Debbie Reynolds.

In school we're learning a two-part song. The boys sing one part, and the girls sing the other. "Come pretty fisher maiden, sailing your boat so free. Look where my castle rises. Will you not marry me?" the boys ask. Then the girls reply, "Seaweed that floats, close by my boat, makes a castle for me. I would not dream of leaving, my home by the shining sea."

I love that the girls say no to the castle. And we say no in big, booming voices, without Miss Nagel having to prompt us to shout out, because all the boys think they're so great.

George Falcone is great, and he's having a Halloween party. He invited Janet and me and everyone else in the whole class. I tell Mama, and she says, "A boy-girl party?

You're nine years old. You're too young. I'm sorry, but you can't go."

I explain that boys and girls are going to be there, but that it's not really a boy-girl party. It's just a party for the kids in our class who happen to be boys and girls. "His parents will be there, Mama. Everyone else in the whole class is going."

"I don't care if everyone else is going. You're only in fifth grade, and you're not."

"Make her let me go," I beg my father when he comes home from work. I follow him into his room where he takes off his police jacket, hangs it in the closet, takes off his holster and unloads his gun. He puts the bullets in a bureau drawer and the gun high up on a shelf. "It's a party for the whole class, Dad. It's not a dance or any-thing. Everyone's going to wear costumes and dunk for apples and stuff like that. If I don't go I'll be the only one who doesn't. Please talk to her, Dad. Please."

I don't know what my father says to Mama, but after a while she comes up to my room and sits next to me on my bed. "I know you think I'm being mean," she says.

"I don't think you're being mean, Mama."

"I just don't want you growing up too fast. You have the whole rest of your life to be a grown-up and to go to parties."

"I know, Mama, but this isn't a grown-up party. It's a kids' party."

Mama looks sad. She looks like she's the one who is about to cry. "Your father says I'm wrong about this. I don't think I'm wrong."

I say nothing. I play with the nubs on my bedspread.

"I couldn't let you go unless I talked to this boy's par-ents first," she says. "And if you go it's only this once. I don't want you coming to me two weeks from now say-ing that so-and-so is having a Christmas party and you want to go to that."

"OK, Mama."

"You're positive the whole class is going?"

I think there are some people who aren't, like Johnny Nelson, because he said he doesn't want to go to a dumb party. I wonder if I should tell Mama this, but I decide I shouldn't, since it's not that Johnny can't go, he doesn't want to go.

"The whole class is going, Mama."

"Then I'm going to make an exception. But just this one time, do you understand?"

"Yes, Mama."

I should feel happy, because my father talked to Mama and I'm getting to go to the party. But I don't feel happy at all. I feel sad, and I don't know why.

●   ●   ●

It's the night of the party, and we're at George Falcone's dunking for apples. There's a big metal bucket full of water and apples on a table in the middle of the room, and we're supposed to put our face into the bucket and bite into an apple. This would be easy, except it isn't when you're blindfolded and your hands are tied behind your back, and there's somebody else who is blindfolded with his hands tied behind his back trying to bite into the same apple at the same time.

This is how the game works: There's a boy on one side of the bucket and a girl on the other. Someone yells, "On your mark, get set, GO!" While blindfolded, you duck, bob and bite, water goes up your nose, and you spit in the bucket. It's kind of disgusting if you don't like the person who's spitting in the bucket with you.

I do. It's George Falcone. I wish I could see him bobbing around in the bucket, but just knowing that his face is in the bucket with mine makes me happy. I bite, and he bites, and we miss. The apples keep rolling around, and the kids are all laughing and cheering us on. I'm hoping that George Falcone's lips will touch my lips accidentally — so it wouldn't be like a kiss or anything. But George bites down and crunch — he's got an apple. The game is over, and our hands and our blindfolds are untied.

Some of the kids' lips do touch, and some of the kids' lips touch intentionally. Everyone laughs louder, and Mrs. Falcone says, "Who wants donuts and cider?" Now everyone is eating.

The party is almost over when George says, "Let's play spin the bottle." We sit in a circle and George spins the bottle. It points at Leo MacNamara, and everyone laughs. So George spins again. It points to Leo again. So Leo takes the bottle and spins it. This time it points to a girl.

Leo leans over and kisses the girl so quickly that I'm not even sure it's a real kiss. Then the girl spins the bottle and it points at George. This time I keep my eyes wide open so I can see if he kisses her or not.

He does. Janet and I glare at this lucky girl whose name we don't know and who must be a neighborhood friend of George's. We've never seen her before, and we're hoping we never see her again.

Now it's George's turn to spin, and Janet and I look at each other hoping it points to one of us. I cross my fingers, and I know she's crossing hers.

But then I hear my mother at the door. I hear her talking to Mrs. Falcone. She's come to get us. Janet and I have to go home.

"Good night, George."

"Good night, Janet. Good night, Beverly."

"Thanks for the party. We had a good time."

The kids are in the corner, and the bottle is spinning as we leave. "How was the party?" Mama says, and we say, "It was fun." Then we don't say anything at all until the next morning as we're walking to church. That's when we wonder out loud, when both of us say over and over on the way to church, during church and on the way home from church, "I wonder if George Falcone's bottle would have pointed to me next."

Grade 5 — Tower Hill Annex

Miss Nagel

Mr. Holmes

Judy Bouzan

Stanley Burwell

Janet Butler

Beverly Curtin

George Falcone

Rosemary Jablonski

Arthur Litchenstein

Johnny Nelson

Michael Ryan

Ann Marie Tantillo

Grace Winters

Your Show of Shows

"I don't want anyone to come to my recital, Mama."
"Why not?" she asks me.

"I don't want to stand up and sing by myself in front of people."

She says I won't be alone, that three other people are going to sing, too.

"But not at the same time, Mama. We're not singing together. Besides, everyone else is older. And I hate the songs I have to sing."

My recital is going to be at Cozy's Steak House, which is a restaurant in the town next to ours. I have never been to a steak house. First we're going to have dinner; then the recital will begin. The singers will perform while everyone else is eating dessert. I'm scheduled to go first with "Bluebird of Happiness." I don't want to go first, but I don't want to go last, either. I don't want to go at all.

"Please don't ask Lorraine or the Nanas to come, Mama. Please don't ask anyone."

Mama says, "I don't understand you. This is a big occasion. But if you don't want anyone there, then we won't invite anyone."

Rose has been picked to be on a radio show that's going to be broadcast all over town, so she's not singing on the show. She has to answer questions like "Who wrote 'Little Women?'" and "What's the capital of Peru." The two smartest kids in Tower Hill School are going to compete with the two smartest kids at Devine School to see which school is smartest. Rose is so smart that she got picked over a whole class of sixth-graders! I tell her I would rather be on a quiz show than in a recital any day. Rose says, "You're crazy, Bev. At least you can practice the songs you're going to sing."

Rose knows all the states and all the capitals, plus the main agricultural product of each. She knows the names of the planets, which is closest to the sun and which is farthest away. She knows how to divide in her head, and she knows every word of "The Midnight Ride of Paul

Revere." I don't think she has anything to worry about.

But she is worried. All she wants to do after school is have me ask her questions.

"Recite President Lincoln's 'Gettysburg Address,' " I say.

"Four score and seven years ago," she begins, then says the whole thing.

"What's a score?" I ask her.

"Twenty years," she replies.

"Who killed President Lincoln?"

"John Wilkes Booth. Stop asking me so many questions about Lincoln. You have to skip around."

I skip around. I ask her hundreds of questions, and she gets every one right.

I sing my songs for her, and she sings them with me. I wish we were singing them together, then performing at Cozy's Steak House wouldn't be so awful and might even be fun.

Her radio show comes before my recital. I sit in the audience with the whole fifth-grade class. I look at Rose up on the stage, and I know how nervous she is. But I'm not worried. She's the smartest girl I know. And she's so pretty in her plaid skirt and light blue sweater, her blonde hair in neat curls that Mrs. Jablonski made with the curling iron.

Mr. and Mrs Jablonski are in the audience; so is Miss Nagel, Mr. Holmes and Mrs. Cormey, and even Rosemary's first-grade teacher, Miss McDonald. There are two students from each school. Arthur Litchenstein is Rosemary's partner.

The Devine School girl is asked to spell "country." "C-o-u-n-t-r-y," she says. What kind of a question is that for a sixth-grader? A second-grader can spell country.

"Who invented the steam engine?"

"Robert Fulton," the other Devine School sixth-grader answers.

Now it's Rose's turn. I am holding my breath and crossing my fingers and saying, "Please, God, please," over and over in my head. Her question is, "Who wrote 'The Midnight Ride of Paul Revere?' " and I relax because I know Rose knows this because she's memorized the entire poem! I wait for the answer, but there's silence instead. Rose isn't saying anything, and I'm wondering, what's wrong? Why isn't she talking?

The man repeats the question. Rose still doesn't say anything, so he turns to the Devine School team and says, "Can you answer that?" A girl says, "Henry Wadsworth Longfellow."

Rose must have been too scared to talk. She must have had stage fright. I look at her up there with her head bowed and I feel so sorry for her because I know she knows the answer. I know she knows all the answers.

She has one more question. It's the last question of the afternoon. Everyone is looking at her. Everyone is tense. "What is paper made of?" the man asks, and I think, paper? What kind of paper. Newspaper? Writing paper? Toilet paper?

I know Rose is in trouble this time because no one has taught us what paper is made of, unless maybe Mr. Holmes has told Rose's class — he's always talking about oxygen and hydrogen and things like that. But I see Rose slump in her chair. Now all I hope is that she doesn't cry.

She raises her head, looks at the man, and says in a tiny voice that I hardly recognize, "Wax?" The man says, "No. I'm sorry," and turns to the people from Devine School again.

Afterward, when the show is over, Rose is silent. All the kids and all the teachers go up to her and say, "It doesn't matter, Rose. You did your best. We're proud of you." But I know how Rose feels. She wants to disappear. She wants to run away and never come back.

She comes to my house because she's sleeping over, and we go up to my room. "No, we don't want any cake now, Mama. No, we don't want any ice cream, either." We sit on my bed, and Rose hugs her knees. She won't look at me, and I don't know what to say.

"I want to go home," she says finally. Then she cries. I know that she's miserable because she never cries, and she never wants to go home when she's here.

"You did your best, Rose. You got the hardest question. No one knows what paper's made of."

"The girl from Devine knew. I should have known."

"She's a whole year older than you."

"I should have known who wrote 'The Midnight Ride of Paul Revere.' Why didn't I?"

"It doesn't matter," I tell her.

"Yes, it does," Rose says, her eyes red, her cheeks wet. "It matters. I want to go home."

I sing my songs at Cozy's Steak House, where the tables are arranged like the desks in my classroom, only instead of making a square, they make a rectangle. I have to stand in the middle of the long end of the rectangle and sing into a microphone. My voice is loud, hollow and not at all like a bluebird's. When I finish, everyone claps, and when the recital is over, everyone says I did a good job. But I am sure I didn't. "I wish you'd continue taking singing lessons," Mama says. But I tell Mama, "You said I could quit after the recital. You promised."

Rose thinks I'm crazy to quit singing lessons. "You like to sing," she argues. I know I like to sing, but I don't like to sing "Bluebird" and "Thee I Love" songs. So I quit, and Mama is quiet for a while.

But one day I come home from school and the record player is on. Mama is singing again, practicing, she says, for the Second Annual North Randolph Minstrel and Variety Show.

"How come you didn't sing in the first one, Mama?" I ask her.

"Because I didn't know about it, so I didn't try out."

Having Mama singing around the house is the best thing. The record player is spinning all the time: in the morning before school, in the afternoon, at night and almost all weekend, and not just Christmas tunes or tunes from plays like "Annie Get Your Gun" and "South Pacific." Mama sings, "I love my baby, my baby loves me. Don't know nobody as happy as we," and "Gonna take a sentimental journey," and "Kiss me once and kiss me twice and kiss me once again, it's been a long, long time."

Some days, when the dining room window is open a little, I can hear the music spilling from the house as I walk up the street. Some days, I can even hear my mother singing along. These are the best days — my favorite times — when I come home to music and my mother is singing.

The Liberace Show

rank is taking me to a Christmas party.

"Uncle Frank," Mama says, correcting me. "He's Uncle Frank."

But Lorraine calls him Frank and Mama calls him Frank, as do my father and Big and Little Nana; everyone calls him Frank. Uncle Frank feels funny on my tongue.

Frank says he doesn't care if I don't call him uncle, but Mama insists that this night I have to say Uncle Frank because he's taking me to a very special father-daughter party.

I wear my Christmas dress, even though it's not Christmas day yet. "It's your holiday dress," Mama says. "That means you can wear it to Christmas parties." I don't want to wear a red bow in my hair, but Mama says a bow makes the outfit. I think the bow looks dumb, that my hair is too short, and that I look like a baby in my frilly red holiday dress.

But when Frank comes, he tells me I look pretty.

I don't know what to say to him in the car. I've never been in the car alone with Frank before. Usually Aunt Lorraine is in the front seat, and I'm in the back. I always have something to say to Lorraine.

Frank talks to me about the party. He says it's a Coast Guard party; that's why he's wearing his navy blue uniform. "All the men will be wearing their uniforms," he says, "so we'll all look alike." I try to imagine a roomful of Franks. I want to ask him why he is taking me to this party instead of Darlene, because she's his daughter, or why Darlene didn't come along, too, because I could have watched her. And it's as if he can read my mind because right then he says, "Lorraine and I thought you'd enjoy this party more than Darlene would. She's a little too young to understand about Christmas yet."

The party is in a big hall, way bigger than the church hall. There are so many chairs and kids and so many Coast Guard people who all look like Frank — in different sizes — that I stay close to my uncle because I don't want to get lost. It's not just a father-daughter party, but a father-son party, too. All the boys are wearing white shirts and ties, even the littlest ones, and they look cute.

I don't know anyone, but Frank knows everyone. People keep coming up and saying, "Hey, Powers! How's it going? Who's the pretty little girl you brought with you?"

Coast Guard people must all be nice.

The first thing we do is wait in a line to get dinner. "This is a buffet dinner," Frank says. "That means you get to pick what you want to eat."

I pick cheese, turkey, ice cream and apple pie. Frank doesn't say, "You have to have vegetables, too." I don't like vegetables, except my mother's mashed potatoes. She whips them and makes them fluffy. Other people's potatoes are lumpy and heavy. Frank must love Coast Guard potatoes; he piles them on his plate, and then he covers them with gravy.

We sit at a long table and eat. Then everybody sings "Silent Night," "The First Noel," "Jingle Bells" and "Santa Claus Is Coming to Town," plus a lot of Christmas songs I don't know.

Then Santa Claus arrives, and it's the real Santa, I can tell, because he's not skinny with a fake beard like Santa's helpers. He's fat and jolly and wears glasses.

Rosemary doesn't believe in Santa, though she doesn't say it straight out. She says, "You can believe what you want to believe, Beverly." Janet says that her mother told her that parents are the real Santas. But my mother swears that Santa is real.

Santa sits high up on a stage, so even though there are people in front of me and we're way back in the hall, I can see him just fine. Santa calls out a name, and a boy goes up on the stage. Santa gives him a present. Then the boy's father goes up on the stage and gives him a present, too.

There are so many children's names being called and so many presents being given out that it takes a long,

long time to call everyone up on the stage. I'm thinking, they're not going to call me because I'm not a daughter, and I don't really belong.

I don't mind not being called. I don't need a present. I'm having fun just being here. I loved the apple pie. But I think maybe Santa might have brought me something anyway, because that's what Santa does. He doesn't forget children. I know Uncle Frank doesn't have a present for me because I would have seen it in the car. And besides, I know Aunt Lorraine and Uncle Frank don't have money to burn. That's what Mama says.

So when Santa does call my name, I'm surprised, but not really. I walk quickly down the aisle, climb up on the stage, take my present and say, "Thank you, Santa." Then I turn to go back to my seat.

But Frank is on the stage, too, and he hands me a small rectangular package. "This is from me," he says. "Merry Christmas." He doesn't kiss me, because Frank isn't mushy like that. He just smiles.

I hurry back to my seat and tear open his present. Now I'm holding a blue velvet box that is so pretty I think it's the present. "Thank you, Uncle Frank," I say. "I love it. It's beautiful."

"You haven't opened it," he says. "That's just the box."

"Just the box?"

"Here. Look inside."

Inside the box are pearls, beautiful pearls, just like the ones Aunt Lorraine has, just like the ones I have tried on sometimes.

"These are for me? They're mine?"

"They certainly are."

"They're exactly like Lorraine's!"

"Well, not quite," Frank says. "But I'm glad you like them."

Like them? I love them. I hug Frank, and then I put them on. I wear them home. I wear them to bed. I wear them to school. I never take them off, not even when I take a bath, not until the string that holds them together breaks. Then I pick up all the pearls, put them in their velvet box and keep them next to my glow-in-the-dark rosary beads, under my Debbie Reynolds scrapbook, in my bureau drawer.

A-Bomb Coverage

On Saturdays my job is to vacuum and dust the parlor. Mama says that to do a good job you have to vacuum everything, not just the tops of cushions and the tops of rugs, but underneath, too. After you vacuum, then you dust. We have a mahogany coffee table with a big glass top, and Mama says, "You can't just clean the top of the glass, Beverly. You have to clean underneath, too."

Getting the glass out of the table is hard. You have to tip it with one hand, catch it with the other and balance it while you clean. "If the phone or the doorbell rings while you're doing this, don't answer it," Mama says.

I get up early every Saturday so I can clean and tip the table and be ready to leave the house right after "Fury." Rose and I walk out our doors at exactly 11:30 so that we can meet halfway. Then we walk downtown. The only times we don't do this is when it's raining hard.

The first thing we do when we get downtown is to stop at the bakery and buy a corn toastie, which we eat on the way to the library. The library is our second stop.

I don't think the librarian likes Rosemary and me. She never lets us go into the adult room, not even when Rose brings a note from her mother that says she has permission to read adult books. "You have to be over twelve to use our adult section," she tells us. "That's the rule, note or no note."

The librarian doesn't approve of the children's books we read, either. She says that YA means young adult, and we are not young adults. "Do your parents know you're reading these books?" she asks us.

We're reading a book by Rosamund DuJardin. We love Rosamund DuJardin. She writes about two girls who are twins and another girl named Darcy. She writes about what they do at school and about their friends and their boyfriends.

Sometimes, after we check out these books, if the librarian is busy with someone else, we sneak into the adult room. But we can only glance at the books there. I wish I could read "A Kiss Before Dying." I saw it at the drive-in last summer, and it was scary. I find it, but I have to put it back quickly because the librarian is not busy anymore. If she catches us where we're not supposed to be, we'll be banned from the library forever.

Rose and I dance down the library steps. They're steep, and they look exactly like the ones James Cagney dances down in "Yankee Doodle Dandy." We sing as we tap, "I'm a Yankee Doodle dandy, a Yankee Doodle do or die."

"SSHHHHHHHH!" the librarian hollers from the top of the stairs, but we continue singing and dancing until we get to the bottom.

Our third stop is the candy store next to the movies. I buy a Charleston Chew, and Rose buys a Bit-O-Honey. We stuff the candy in our pockets because you're not supposed to take candy into the movie theater. You're supposed to buy it there. But candy bars at the movie cost a dime, and next door they're a nickel. Who would pay a dime when you can get the same thing for a nickel? Today we are going to see "The Spider" and "The Day the World Ended."

"The Spider" comes on first. It's pretty scary when the girl gets stuck in the giant spider web since the web is big and sticky. But I know it's just a movie. Rose and I love horror movies. We laugh at them. When we saw "The Creature From the Black Lagoon," we laughed out loud at the scariest parts. Even "Invasion of the Body Snatchers" didn't frighten us. Not much anyway.

But I am very scared watching "The Day the World Ended." A big bomb goes off and kills practically everyone in the world. One of the survivors is a pretty girl who thinks the bomb has killed her handsome boyfriend. But he isn't dead. He's been turned into an ugly monster. People die if they even go near him because he's full of radiation. When the girl finds out that this monster is her boyfriend, it's the worst thing. She wants to go to him, but she can't.

Rose says, "It's only a movie, Beverly." I cover my eyes anyway, and when it's over and the lights come on, I'm still scared.

It's not real, I say, inside my head. If a bomb fell on a person it would kill them dead. It wouldn't turn them into a monster. There are no monsters. I know that.

But I'm not so sure right now. I have to get up out of my seat and walk outside. Mr. Jablonski is waiting for us. It gets dark early now, and we're not allowed to walk home. We're not afraid of the dark, we tell our parents. But all of a sudden, I am afraid. I'm afraid of the dark for the first time since I was little, since the ghosts came into my bedroom and wouldn't leave.

Rose says, "It was a creepy movie, wasn't it?"

I look out the car window as Mr. Jablonski drives past the theater, the A&P and Leon's and Rosemary's church. I think about how a bomb could make all these buildings disappear. I'm scared because I know that being in the car with Mr. Jablonski won't keep me safe and that being home with my mother won't keep me safe. If the bomb comes, nothing will keep me safe and I'll disappear, too.

My house is dark when we pull up in front of it. Not even the kitchen light is on. Shane barks and jumps up and licks me. Where is my mother?

"Mama?" I say into the darkness. "Mama?"

I turn on the light and walk down the hall. I hear my footsteps on the hardwood floor. The house is silent. Too silent.

I wish that my father weren't at work and that my mother were in the kitchen singing along with Patti Page, all the lights on, dinner cooking. I wish that I could stop thinking about the movie, all the dead people and the horrible monster.

"It's just a movie. It isn't real," I say out loud, and my voice startles me.

"Beverly? Is that you?" Mama says.

She's in the bedroom, in bed, under the covers. "Why

are you sleeping? Are you sick?" I ask.

"I'm just tired," she says. "I don't know why. Can you get your own dinner? Would you mind?"

I don't want to get my own dinner. I want my mother to get up, come into the kitchen, make me a grilled cheese sandwich, talk to me and make the monster go away.

"Are you all right, Baybo?"

"Yes, Mama. I'm fine."

"Then I'm going to rest for a while, OK?"

"Sure," I say.

I walk into the parlor and turn on the lights, then walk upstairs and turn on more lights. I take off my shoes, flop on the bed and close my eyes, but I have to sit up and open them because the monster's there grinning at me.

I carry my desk chair over to the window and look outside at the street light and the way the air looks thick, like fog, underneath it. Just like the fog in the movie. Just like the radiation.

What if this were radiation? What if Lewis Drive, Davis Road and Grove Street, where Rosemary lives, were all gone? What if a bomb came and killed everyone except me? What if I were the only one left in the whole world?

It starts to rain — a cold, hard sleet — and the rain bangs against the window. The fog drips, and the furnace groans. No place is safe. Not outside. Not inside. Not anywhere.

I change into my pajamas, tiptoe downstairs and creep into my mother's room. I don't want to make dinner. I don't want to do anything except lie beside my mother and wait for my father to come home.

Have a Heart

Rose says that worrying about a war is stupid, that there won't be a war and that "The Day the World Ended" was only a dumb movie.

I say, "OK, so how come people are building fallout shelters all over the place?"

"What people?" Rose says. "Who do you know who is building a fallout shelter? Who do you know who has ever even SEEN a fallout shelter?"

I ask Miss Nagel if she knows anyone who has a fallout shelter. She says no and that I shouldn't worry about things like radiation and an atomic war. "At your age," she says, "you should be thinking about Valentine's Day, not the end of the world."

Later, she announces to the whole class that we can have a Valentine's Day party. We get to bring in cupcakes, candy and Coke, plus Valentine cards for everyone in the room. I've already picked out the card I'm going to give George Falcone. I have it in my desk. It says, "You're cute."

Janet squeals when I tell her this. "You're not really going to give him a card that says that, are you? You're just fooling, right?"

I take out the card and hand it to her. It's a teddy bear that, when you open it, says "You're cute" and that I've already signed, "LOVE, BEVERLY." Janet shrieks, and Miss Nagel turns and looks sharply at us.

"What's the rule about talking while someone else is talking, girls?"

"Sorry, Miss Nagel," we chime.

She continues telling us about the party. "It would be nice if you all wore something red, don't you think?"

All the girls shout yes, because we think it's a great idea, but the boys groan. Miss Nagel ignores them and continues. "Whose mother will make cupcakes?" and my hand shoots up. My mother makes the best cupcakes. Everyone says so.

Miss Nagel makes a list on the blackboard and writes

everything down: who will bring Coke and who will bring napkins. This takes a long time because the whole class has to bring something.

Then Miss Nagel says she has a special announcement. "At the end of the party, boys and girls, we're going to have a contest, and the winner will get," and she reaches into her desk drawer, "this chocolate heart."

It's a big heart, the kind that's always on the top shelf at the drug store, the kind that you can look at but never touch. It's in a red box with a red bow. Even though it's not solid milk chocolate, which is my favorite, and even though I never win anything, I hope I win this heart.

"Oh, I hope I win it," I say out loud to Janet. "I really, really want to win." Bobby Fletcher, who sits next to me on my other side hears me, and because he likes me, he says, "I hope you win, too."

Miss Nagel doesn't hear Bobby Fletcher talking, but she hears me. All of a sudden she's taking giant steps across the room, a scowl on her forehead, the puncher in hand. "That'll be five punches, Beverly. I gave you fair warning."

I hand her my conduct card. She punches one, two, three, four, five. The class is silent. Five punches are a lot. My card looks like Swiss cheese. I know I'm in trouble.

I don't talk the rest of the day. I don't even raise my hand to answer questions. Maybe if I never talk again and never get one more punch, and everyone else talks a lot and gets lots of punches, the whole class will get bad marks in conduct and Mama won't be so mad at me.

I try to keep quiet all the time. I try real hard, but the words just fall out. I tell Mama this. But she says that words don't fall out, that they have to be pushed out and that I do way too much pushing.

When I go home I tell Mama all about the Valentine party and about the big heart that Miss Nagel is going to give away. I tell her that everyone's going to wear red and that the kids want her to make the cupcakes. I even tell her that I'm going to give George Falcone a Valentine that says, "You're cute."

But I don't tell her about the punch card. I figure that she's going to find out about this soon enough.

George Falcone gives me the best Valentine. It's a big fuzzy heart, and it says, "Be Mine." In George's writing are the most important words: "Love, George."

"Janet, look! Look at what George gave me." I see him across the room, meet his eyes and smile, and he smiles back. Janet is opening a card. "Hey, look at the card George gave me." It's a big fuzzy heart that says, "Be Mine," and it's signed, "Love George." AND IT IS EXACTLY LIKE MINE!

I look and see George smiling at Janet now. Bobby Fletcher taps my shoulder. "Did you open my card yet?"

"No, Bobby. It must be in my pile."

Everyone has a pile because everyone had to bring in cards for everyone in the whole room. It takes a long time to open the cards and to eat cupcakes and candy and drink Coke.

Finally it's time for the contest. Miss Nagel told us before lunch that she was going to write down a number between one and a hundred on a piece of paper and that she would go around the room and give us all a chance to guess that number. I don't know what number I'm going to pick. I count the buttons on my red blouse: five. I count the letters in my name: thirteen. I think, maybe I should say forty-seven because I was born in 1947.

Bobby Fletcher leans over and whispers, "Say seven."

"What?"

"Say seven. You want to win the heart, don't you? I saw her write it down."

But how could Bobby Fletcher, who sits far away from Miss Nagel, have seen her write down anything? I think he's just saying this. But why?

Around the room Miss Nagel goes. Thirty-six? Fifty-five? Ten? One? Seventy-nine? Twelve? Now it's Bobby

Fletcher's turn, and he says seventeen. Why doesn't he say seven if he saw her write it down? Why would he give the heart to me? I know he likes me, but this is a great, big, wonderful, chocolate Valentine heart.

"Beverly?" Miss Nagel says. "It's your turn."

I look at Bobby. Bobby looks at me. "Say it," he says. "Say it."

"Seven!" I shout. Miss Nagel holds up the piece of paper, and, sure enough, there it is, the number seven.

"That's not fair. I didn't get a turn," Janet says, and it really isn't fair. But I don't care, because I won the heart, and I've never won anything in my whole entire life.

I walk up to Miss Nagel's desk, and she hands me the heart. I turn around and head back to my desk and George Falcone says, "I hope you're gonna share that." I say, in my meanest voice, "Not with you."

Bobby doesn't ask to share the heart. He says, "Did you like my Valentine card?" I don't remember his card, but I say, "Yes, I liked it." I don't want to hurt his feelings because he could have said seven and then I wouldn't have won.

I eat the heart later. I share it with Janet, Rose and my mother. Even my father, who doesn't like candy, has a taste. It's a big, big heart, and I don't mind sharing it all.

Rose says, "You're so lucky you had a party."

Janet says, "You're so lucky you won."

I don't tell Janet, Rose or my mother or my father that I wasn't lucky, that Bobby Fletcher told me to say seven. But I tell Father Finn, because if Bobby really saw the number, then this was cheating, and cheating is a sin.

Father Finn says, "Don't worry about the heart. It was not a sin. It was probably just a lucky guess."

But I say three "Hail Marys" and three "Our Fathers," just in case.

Sing It Again

I am giving up candy and movies for Lent this year and am offering up my sacrifice for the souls in Purgatory.

Rose says, "Why can't you just give up candy?"

That's what I usually do. But I love the movies just as much as I love Chunkies and Charleston Chews, and Lent is about sacrifice, Father Finn says, so I need to do both things.

Rose says that there's no such thing as Purgatory and that it's silly to not go to the movies for two whole months to help people in Purgatory if there isn't any Purgatory. Besides, who will she go to the movies with if I don't go?

Janet and I know there's a Purgatory and that it's a terrible place where people are sent if they can't get into Heaven. Purgatory is not as bad as Hell because Hell is forever. You burn there for eternity. But in Purgatory, if people pray for you, you don't have to spend as much time in the flames.

I love the movies, I love candy, and I love Rosemary best of all, but I think about these people in Purgatory having to jump into the fires before they get into Heaven. I also think how great it is that if I give up Chunkies and movies, then someone may not have to do this.

My mother is giving up cigarettes again. My father is giving up highballs because he already gave up cigarettes a few years ago and now he doesn't smoke anymore.

Janet and I are going to make a novena, too. A novena is when you go to church for nine nights in a row. Noveni means nine in Latin. That's why they call it a novena, Father Finn said. He said everyone should try to make one sometime.

My mother is practicing for the Minstrel Show. A Minstrel Show is when people get up on a stage and sing, dance and play instruments. Most nights my father drives my mother to Randolph High School, sits in the auditorium and listens as she sings. My father loves listening to my mother sing. He plays the record that she made him over and over. "You're going to wear it out, Larry," my mother says.

Aunt Lorraine is in the Minstrel Show, too. She's going to be a package of cigarettes that comes out on the stage and says, "Why don't you pick me up and smoke me sometime?" She doesn't sing this. She just says it. But Mama says she is great.

Mama is singing two songs: one with two other ladies and one all by herself. "I love my baby, my baby loves me. Don't know nobody, as happy as we." This is her solo. I've never seen my mother sing on a stage, though I know she has. Once, when she was dating my father, she sang in a talent show and won first prize. My father was in the audience then, too, Mama said.

Now I am in the audience sitting next to my father, who is all dressed up in a jacket and a tie. I am dressed up, too. The whole audience looks dressed for a party.

The band starts to play, the curtain rises, and the show begins. There's Ann Marie's mother, Chickey Fleming's mother, Mrs. Schoepplein, Mrs. Joseph and Mrs. Montecalvo. The stage is full of mothers, and they are all singing and dancing: "Hello, hello, hello again. Time to start the show again. Thank you for coming and how do you do? Oh, how we've missed you the whole year through."

Mrs. Tantillo is usually in the kitchen cooking or squeezing clean clothes through her wringer washing machine. I didn't know she could sing and dance. I wonder if Ann Marie knew.

My mother doesn't come on for a long time, not until the second act. I like watching everyone else's mother — they're all really, really good — but I wish my mother could have her turn now. I can't wait to see her.

When she does come out on the stage, I don't recognize her. My father has to say, "There she is, Bev. Look!" I saw her costume at home on a hanger, but not on her.

It's short, red and fringy, and she's wearing black, lacy nylons and red high heels. She's kicking like a June Taylor dancer and singing in a loud voice.

I can't take my eyes off her. I want to turn to my father and say, "Did you know she could do this?" but I can't. I might miss something. She is such a good dancer. How come she never dances at home?

Her voice doesn't surprise me. It's what I hear almost every day. But it's only her voice that I recognize up on the stage. I wouldn't know this was my mother except for the sound of her.

When she's finished, the crowd applauds for a long time. Then Aunt Lorraine walks on the stage with a bunch of other women dressed like cigarettes — but Aunt Lorraine is the prettiest. She says her line, and everyone laughs. Then Mama's back on the stage singing a song that I don't know. This time she's not dancing; she's swaying and singing with two other women who have their arms around each other's waists. Now Mama is wearing a light pink, shiny dress that she bought in Central Square, and I can tell it's my mother. I turn to my father and smile.

Then Mama comes on one more time, with a handsome man, and I'm surprised. "What's she doing, Dad? This isn't in the program." But he's not surprised. I can tell he's seen this before.

Mama sings, "Gonna take a sentimental journey, gonna set my heart at ease. Gonna take a sentimental journey, to renew old memories."

Then the man sings, too: "Got my bag and got my reservation. Spent each dime I could afford." And then he puts his arm around my mother, and they are singing and swaying together! "Seven, that's the time we leave at seven. I'll be waiting up for Heaven." I think that my mother could be a movie star, she is so pretty, and her voice is so sweet. And I'm glad that there's another show tomorrow night so I can see it all over again. I wish there were shows every night so my mother could sing and dance and look so pretty and happy all the time.

The crowd leaps to its feet when they finish. Then the finale begins. There is hooting and hollering, and my father and I are up on our feet. Here comes Uncle Frank and he says, "Weren't they wonderful?" And we are hooting and hollering, too.

Now she is back in the kitchen, my mother again. She's wearing a housedress and an apron. Ezio Pinza is singing "This Nearly Was Mine." This is my mother's favorite song from "South Pacific."

"When you were young, did you want to be a singer, Mama?" I ask.

"No, not really. I like to sing, but I just wanted to be a mother."

"If you were a singer, you'd be rich," I say.

"If I were a singer, I might not have you."

Mama and me

Easter Parade

*R*osemary did peppers playing jump rope at recess today. Then she went home, and her appendix exploded.

Her mother told my mother that Rose's appendix exploded in the doctor's hands. Is it because she did so many peppers? Are peppers dangerous, too, I wonder?

I don't ask my mother because she thinks everything's dangerous. I don't want her to make a connection between peppers and an appendix or she'll never let me jump rope again. I feel so sorry for Rose because having your appendix out hurts a lot, my mother said. I feel guilty, too, because I was jealous when she beat me at peppers.

I can't visit her at the hospital, even though my father said he would take me, because I'm not old enough. You have to be fourteen to visit someone in the hospital. That's the rule. I think this is the dumbest thing, like not being able to go in the adult section at the library. Who makes up these rules anyway? Maybe if I wore lipstick and nylons I'd look fourteen, I tell my mother. But she says, "You'll do no such thing, Beverly. Besides, you couldn't look fourteen if you tried."

I think that the boy who whistled at me the other day thought I was fourteen. I was walking to the halfway point to meet Rose, and a boy driving a black truck leaned out the window and whistled. Then he slowed down and asked me if I had any older sisters at home. I said, "No, I don't," and he drove away.

Rose said it's because I need a bra. "Boys whistle at girls with breasts," she said. But I don't need a bra, and I don't want one. I don't like Rose talking about breasts.

When you wear a bra, the boys at the bus stop snap the back of it right when you're getting on the bus and your hands are full of books, so you can't hit them. If I wore a bra in the fifth grade it would be the most horrible thing. No one in the whole entire Tower Hill Annex wears a bra, except Miss Nagel.

I wear undershirts, two of them. This way I don't bounce when I walk. Rose said I probably need to wear three undershirts if I don't want boys in black trucks whistling at me.

When Rose comes home from the hospital, I walk over after school and visit her. She won't show me her scar, though I beg. She says it's huge and ugly, and she doesn't want me to see it.

"Did it hurt to have your appendix out?"

"It hurt a lot," Rose says.

"Do you think it exploded because you did so many peppers?"

"I don't know, but I'm never doing peppers again."

I can't eat candy, but Rose can, so I give her my whole box of chocolate-covered marshmallow eggs that I've been saving under my bed for Easter morning.

"How come it's open?"

"Because when I'm missing candy the most, I smell the eggs, and smelling them is almost as good as eating them."

"That's disgusting," Rose says.

"I don't lick them, Rose. I only smell them. Do you want them or not?"

• • • •

I can't wear nylons on Easter Sunday, and everyone else can. Rose, Janet, Ann Marie and even Michelle, who is only in FOURTH GRADE, are all wearing nylons and shoes with no straps.

I have to wear ankle socks and my ugly baby shoes. I'd rather stay in the house all day. I'd rather be sick in bed than have to go to church on Easter Sunday looking like a two year old, when everyone else is going to look so nice.

"They're not going to look nice," Mama says. "They're going to look ridiculous. They're little girls, Beverly. They don't have anything to hold up nylons. They'll bag at the ankles, you mark my words. You're not wearing them, so stop asking. You'll have plenty of time for nylons when you're grown-up."

But I don't want to grow up. I just want to wear nylons like all the kids. "They have garter belts to hold up the nylons, Mama. Janet showed me hers. Please, please, please can't I wear them just on Easter and just to church? I'll take them off right after Mass. I'll dry the dishes every night for a week. Oh, please, Mama, please?"

But she says, "No, and that's that. I don't want to talk about it anymore." I say, "Can I at least have shoes without straps?" She says no to that, too, because my heels turn inward and I need a Thomas lift, and what good is a Thomas lift if you have shoes that you can walk right out of?

Oh, how I dread Easter Sunday. Janet, Ann Marie and Michelle are all wearing suits, too. Suits, nylons and shoes without straps. And I'm wearing a frilly dress, ankle socks and patent leather shoes. I think maybe, if I'm lucky, I'll get the mumps.

But on Easter Sunday I wake up healthy, no temperature, no swollen glands. I say to Mama, "Is it OK if we go to 11:30 Mass?"

Eleven-thirty is the last Mass, and no one likes to go to this because it means not eating all the way from midnight. Fasting this long, especially on Easter when there's candy waiting for you, is not something most people choose. But my mother likes 11:30 Mass because Father Kelleher says it, and she likes him. So she's excited that I want to go to 11:30. "Are you sure you won't get too hungry waiting?" she says. "Don't you want to dig into your Easter basket?"

"No, Mama. I can wait. I'll be fine," I say.

I watch TV for a while, and then I go into the dining room and look out the window. In a little while I know that Ann Marie, Janet and Michelle will come out of their houses and meet on the corner, and I want to see how pretty they look.

Janet and Ann Marie come out first. I look hard to see if their nylons are bagging at their ankles, but I can't tell. All I see is that they look nice and that they're smiling. Then Michelle comes running down her front steps. There they are, the three of them, looking so grown-up. I move behind the curtain so they can't see me sitting inside wishing I were out there with them. But I peek at them until they turn the corner, until I can no longer see them. Then I go upstairs and get dressed.

Mama and me in our Easter dresses

Star Time

*E*very day when my father comes home from work, after he hangs up his uniform and changes into regular clothes, he marches up the steps and goes into his "office." It's not a real office. It's just a place big enough for a desk at the top of the steps. He's studying to be a police sergeant. He has piles of police books thick with words I don't understand, but he says he likes reading them. It's the English grammar books he doesn't like. "You pay attention in school so you won't end up not knowing when to use who or whom," he tells me.

My father prints words on index cards, writes their definitions on the back, then memorizes the definitions. My job is to ask him these definitions.

"What is allegiance?"

"Allegiance is the obligation of fidelity and obedience which an individual owes to the country of which he is a citizen and to which he is a native," he replies.

"What is an infant?"

"An infant is any person under twenty-one."

"Really?"

"Really," my father says.

"What is a pyromaniac?"

"A pyromaniac is a person who has a compulsion to set fires."

"What is a kleptomaniac?"

"A kleptomaniac is a person who has a compulsion to steal things."

It isn't on one of his cards, but I ask my father, what does compulsion mean?

"It means you have a need to do these things."

"Why would anyone need to set a fire?"

"I don't know, Beverly. Just ask the questions."

Mama has a new job working at Wethern's in Quincy, which is a city close to Boston. She is a milliner now.

"What's a milliner?" Rosemary asks when I phone and tell her.

"It's a person who makes and sells hats." I say this as

if I knew all along, as if I didn't have to ask my mother the very same thing.

"Your mother makes hats?"

"Mostly she sells them, but sometimes she makes them. She puts veils and flowers on them. Want to come over and see?"

Mama wears a hat every day — to work, at work and home from work. She looks nice in a hat; that's what my father says. I think some of the hats look like flying saucers, but Mama says flat hats with wide brims are stylish.

Mama works every day except Wednesday and Sunday. On Wednesdays, if it's hot and sunny, she takes Rose and me to Nantasket Beach. We don't have to beg her, she likes the beach. But she never goes in the water when she gets there. She lies on a blanket on the sand. I say, "Aren't you hot, Mama?" and she says "No. The sun feels nice."

I can't imagine lying on a blanket and not going in the ocean when it's right there calling to you. I can't imagine being a grownup.

I don't want to grow up. I want to stay ten years old and best friends with Rosemary forever, collecting bottles at the beach, cashing them in for money, then going over to the amusement park to spend it.

"Don't be gone long," Mama always says. "Be careful."

"Want to come with us, Mama?"

"No, I'm fine here."

Imagine not wanting to ride the rocket ship or the Tilt-a-Whirl!

Rose and I are putting on a big summer Talent Show in my back yard. We're in charge, but anyone who wants to can be in it. Janet, Ann Marie, Michelle and Elaine Maganello say they want to be in it. Elaine also says that she is now positive that her doll isn't alive. It was her brother who put the poop in her doll's diaper, she tells me.

I don't ask where her brother got the poop because I

do not want to know. I don't play with Elaine much any-more, but she says she wants to be in our Talent Show.

People who want to see our Talent Show will have to pay a nickel, just like they had to pay for the Minstrel Show. This is Rose's idea. She says we'll be rich. When I'm rich I'm going to buy tons of Little Lulu comic books.

Our opening number is "Hello, Hello, Hello Again." It's the same song the Minstrel Show people used, but the dance that goes with it is different. Rose and I are the only ones in the opening number because no one has come over to practice. We're in my back yard on the cement patio. It has my last year's handprint in it because that's when my father made the patio. My mother's statue of the Virgin Mary, which is guarding her rock garden, is looking over us. It's a very hot day. Shane is asleep in the shade.

Rose and I practice our dance. She starts at one end of the patio, and I start at the other. We skip our way to the middle in tune to the song, then we shuffle-ball-change all the way to the end.

It's a great opening. So what if we stole it from the Minstrel Show. It looks so different in my back yard that I feel as if the Minstrel Show people stole it from us!

The next song we practice is "Tammy." If I were to go into Boston with my mother and make a record right now, I would sing "Tammy." I love Tammy. I sing the first verse, and Rose sings the second. "Whip-poor-will, whip-poor-will, you and I know, Tammy, Tammy, can't let him go. The breeze from the bayou keeps murmuring low, Tammy, Tammy, you love him so."

If I close my eyes I can see Debbie Reynolds in my back yard singing away because Rose's voice is the exact same. She even gurgles like Debbie Reynolds in the whip-poor-will part. Rosemary can do everything. She can even sing like a movie star.

We print up tickets for our Talent Show. We make a poster and tape it to Gilroy's window. Soon Janet, Ann

Marie, Michelle and Chickey Fleming start coming to our practices.

Janet says, "I want to sing 'Wanted,' " so she's singing in our show and Ann Marie is dancing. We're not sure what Michelle is going to do because she can't decide. But there's plenty of time for her to make up her mind because our Minstrel Show is still three whole weeks away.

We practice, but not every day. Some days Rose and I catch butterflies or praying mantises and put them in jars. Some days we search the lawn for four-leaf clovers. My mother says if you find a four-leaf clover and carry it with you at all times, you'll have nothing but good luck. If I find a four-leaf clover I'm going to give it to Mama, because if she had some luck maybe she could have a baby like Vera Campbell did. Mama said Vera was lucky to have a baby after all these years, and though Rose doesn't think a four-leaf clover had anything to do with Vera Campbell's having a baby, she helps me look anyway.

Some days Rose and I play in the woods behind the School for the Deaf. Besides practicing for the Minstrel Show and going to the beach, playing in the woods is my favorite thing. Mama doesn't know Rose and I do this. I don't tell her because she'd say, "I don't want you in the woods, Beverly. It's too dangerous." But it isn't. To get into the woods, Rose and I have to walk past Ann Marie's house and cross Chestnut Street, then cut through the Yount's field where everyone goes sledding in the winter. Then we walk behind the houses on Chestnut Circle into the woods, where we follow a narrow path to a stream.

In the spring, the stream is wide, and we build a bridge across it out of rocks and fallen branches. But it's practically dry, now, more mud than water, so all we have to do is step across. Then we follow another smaller path, and then there's no path at all. We get to a small clearing. Sometimes we stop there because the grass is soft, and we can lie on it and watch the clouds roll by. Sometimes we stop at the pond behind the school because it's shady and cool and full of lily pads.

But our favorite place to sit for a long time is under a tree in the side yard of the school. It's a big tree on top of a big hill, and though you can see the traffic from North Main Street, you can't hear anything except birds singing. Once in a while we'll see a sister hurrying out of the school, and I'll think, she's going to tell us, "This is private property, girls. I really must ask you to leave." But she never does.

Rose and I would stay under this tree forever. It's perfect here, a perfect place to plan your whole life. And that's what we do. We dream, and we plan. Some days we talk about changing our names, buying wigs and running away to California to be movie stars. Other days Rose says she wants to be a lawyer and have two children instead. No matter how our plans change, one thing never does. When we're sitting under that tree, and we say the same word at the same time and link our little fingers to make a wish, I know that we're wishing the same thing: that no matter what we grow up to be, we will always be best friends.

• • • •

It rains the day before the Minstrel Show, so our last practice is cancelled. My mother is at work. Rose is at home. Ann Marie is on vacation at a cottage with her whole family. I phone Janet, but no one answers. There's nothing on TV. I've read all my Little Lulu comic books, and I have nothing to do.

So I decide to look through the photo albums that are in my mother's bottom bureau drawer. I love looking at the old black-and-white pictures of my mother and father. My father takes slides now. He has to set up a projector in the parlor, and we have to look at the pictures on the parlor wall because we don't have a screen.

When you look at the pictures on the wall they look funny. There are big purple flowers on our wallpaper, and those flowers get into all the pictures. My father says that when we get a screen, I will definitely like the slides better than ordinary old pictures because slides are big and colorful. But I think he's wrong. I like the black-and-white-pictures and being able to go into my mother's bureau drawer by myself whenever I want.

I take out the pictures of my mother when she was young. I think how she always says, "I wasn't born old, you know," but I really think she was. I can't imagine my mother ten years old, though she swears she once was ten and though I am holding a picture of her when she wasn't much older. But it doesn't look like my mother in the picture. It looks like her face, but her hair is in these funny tight curls and she's wearing a print dress and striped socks. My mother would never mix prints and stripes.

The rain stops, and a rainbow cuts through the sky. I put away the pictures, grab my sneakers and race outside so I can follow the rainbow to its end. Finding the end of a rainbow is hard, like finding a four-leaf clover. Sometimes I think I'm close, but when I get to where the end should be, the rainbow is always gone.

Today I run all the way down Althea Road past where they're building new houses before the rainbow's end disappears. It should be right behind this new house. Why isn't it? Why does it do this? Where does it go? I don't know what I'd do if I found the pot of gold. Gold is heavy. How would I carry it home?

I don't know, but every time there's a rainbow, I look for the end. Someone has to find it someday. And maybe, instead of a pot of gold too heavy to carry home, I'd find a stream full of fresh rain and a baby in a basket floating by.

Kid Gloves

I have so many Little Lulu books now that when I pile them on the bookshelf my father made they fall over. I have old ones, new ones and even big, fat twenty-five-cent ones.

Rose put her Talent Show money in a silver pig that one of her relatives gave her. She doesn't love Little Lulu the way I do.

All the mothers came to our Talent Show, and some of them paid a whole quarter, not just a nickel, to watch us sing and dance. Mama made lemonade because it was a hot, hot day, and she served it for free. I wanted to charge another nickel, but she said no.

It's hot today, so hot you could fry an egg on the sidewalk. That's what Mama says. "Who would want to fry an egg on the sidewalk?" I ask, and she says that it's just an expression, but that she really can't remember when it was this hot.

When she comes home from work, she takes off her dress, puts on a house coat and sits at the kitchen table in front of the fan. I ask, "What's for dinner?" She says, "It's too hot to eat, Beverly," which means I can make myself a bologna and cheese sandwich instead of having to eat something like steak and salad.

The next day is Wednesday. It's still hot, but we don't go to the beach this week. Mama says it's time to go school shopping. Only three more weeks until school starts. So we have to go, heat or no heat.

School is going to be very different this year. I wish we could go back to Tower Hill Annex and have it be the same because Miss Nagel is the best teacher and fifth grade was the best year. But now I'm going into sixth grade, and it's back to Tower Hill School, but not for the whole day. There are so many of us sixth-graders, because so many kids moved into Randolph over the summer, that we're going to be on double sessions. This means that half the class will go to school in the morning from eight o'clock to noon, and the other half will go from 12:30 to 4:30. In January, those going in the morning will switch to the afternoon.

It's a great plan; there will be so many extra hours to play if Rose and I get in the same class. But what if we don't? What if she goes mornings and I go afternoons? Then we'll never see each other because she'll be home when I'm in school and I'll be home when she's in school. It will be the worst thing.

Mama says I shouldn't worry about it, that I have lots of other friends. But I don't know how she can say this; she knows that Rose is my very best friend.

We're supposed to get a letter in the mail telling us what teacher we have and whether we'll start the year going mornings or afternoons. I don't care about mornings or afternoons. The only thing I care about is that Rose is in my class.

I am in the dressing room at Conrad and Chandler trying on a maroon plaid dress that's too tight at the top when the saleslady says to Mama, "I think your daughter needs a bra."

I think I'm going to die right here in the small, stuffy dressing room. I think I might even want to die because I don't need a bra, and why is this lady saying this?

I'm wearing my three T-shirts, and I'm pretty flat if I look straight at myself. It's only when I turn to the side that you can see two big lumps. But there is no way I am going to wear a bra to school. I'd rather not go to school. I'd rather never see Rosemary again.

The saleslady returns with a huge, ugly bra. Mama says, "Why don't you just try it on, Baybo." I say, "No, Mama, I want to go home."

The saleslady is practically in the dressing room with me, and I'm wondering why my mother isn't telling her to get out — that's what I want to say. I'm standing there in the ugliest, tightest, babiest plaid dress ever, and this lady with red hair, not like Little Nana's, but ugly red, is shoving a big, fat bra at me. I don't know whether to scream or cry or do both.

Mama finally says, "We don't need that, thank you," and tells me to put on my clothes. We're leaving here.

We walk over to Colestone's without talking. I am mad at my mother. Why did she let that saleslady say I need a bra? Why didn't she say, "No, she doesn't. She's just a little girl."

Mama says when we're waiting in line, "You can have anything you want," but all I get is a root beer because I'm not hungry. I want an ice cream, but I don't want to eat one. Then Mama will think I'm OK and I'm not.

We sit down, and she knows I'm not OK. "That lady embarrassed you, didn't she?" she says.

I say nothing because, if I talk, I know I'll cry.

"I should have told her to take her bra and shove it."

I look at Mama and smile.

"You don't have to wear a bra if you don't want to."

"I don't want to, Mama."

"I know you wouldn't want anyone to know you were wearing a bra."

I think maybe my mother does understand.

"I suppose, if you decided to wear one, you'd have to wear a T-shirt over it or a full-length crinoline because those have the same shoulder straps, and then no one would know."

"Rose has a crinoline with thick shoulder straps. It's really pretty," I say.

Mama sips on her iced coffee, and we're both silent.

"Maybe we should go back to a different department and try on some skirts and blouses. You didn't look through those yet, did you?"

"You mean I don't have to get a dress?"

"Not if you find a skirt you like better."

I finish my root beer, and we walk back to Conrad and Chandler. I pick out a plaid skirt, not because I know Mama will like it, but because I like it. I get a red, long-sleeve, button-down-the-front sweater to match; dark red shoes; long socks; and two dresses that have great wide skirts. Mama says, "How about if we get you a crinoline like Rose's?"

I have lots of crinolines at home, but they're half-crinolines, not full ones. Mama says, "Here, try this on," and I go back into the dressing room and slip on the crinoline. It's the prettiest thing. I put my T-shirt on top of it, but the T-shirt wrecks the way the crinoline looks, so I put my T-shirt under it, and that looks better.

We go home, and I take all my new clothes and hang them in my closet. When I'm done I come downstairs and help Mama set the table.

She says, "I don't want you to be mad at me, but I bought you something else."

"What's that, Mama?" I ask.

"You don't have to wear it. You can just put it in your drawer until you decide you want to."

She hands me a bra, not the big, ugly one that the saleslady had, but another one that's not quite as ugly with a tiny, pink, satin rose on the front.

"I don't want you to grow up either," Mama says. "I don't like this any more than you do."

I cry then, after trying not to cry all day. Mama hugs me, and she cries, too.

The Power of Women

*R*ose thinks it's neat that I have a bra. I think she's crazy. "I'd wear it in a second," she says, "and I wouldn't bother putting a slip over it."

Rose is as flat and as skinny as a Popsicle stick. I look like a snow cone: big from the feet up, big everywhere, biggest at the top.

Aunt Lorraine says that breasts are a good thing to have and that I should stand up straight and not apologize for them. She says that she got her first bra going into sixth grade and that she didn't mind. But I mind.

Mama tells me something that's even worse than having a bra. She says that when little girls get to be big girls, they get a visit from a friend.

"What kind of a friend?" I ask, thinking won't it be nice if this friend is Mary Toomey and she comes to visit? But Mama says this is a different kind of friend, that when girls get breasts they also get this friend who visits them once a month. She says when your friend comes to visit, you bleed.

You bleed? I say. Where? Why?

Mama says you bleed on your underpants, so nobody knows. But you have to wear a special pad. She shows me this big, fat, cottony thing that looks like a huge Band-Aid, and then she shows me this elastic thing you have to use with it.

"Do you have any questions?" she asks me. I say no because I don't know what to ask except, what does a friend coming to visit have to do with any of this?

She says that "friend" is our secret name and that I can say to her any time, "Mama, my friend has come to visit," and no one will know what I'm talking about except us.

I tell Rose about this. She says she has always wondered what those Band-Aid things were for, that her mother has a boxful in their bathroom.

But when I tell Janet and Ann Marie, they're not surprised. They say, "Oh, that's just the period at the end of a sentence." I say, "What?" They repeat, "That's just the

PERIOD at the end of the sentence." and then they laugh and laugh.

"Period's what you call it," Janet says. "That's the real name."

"The real name?"

They nod, and I don't say a word. I go on home because I can't figure out what a period at the end of a sentence has to do with anything.

A week before school starts, the mailman brings the letter I've been waiting for. I am on morning sessions, and I have Mr. O'Neil. Rosemary doesn't know who she has yet because her mailman doesn't deliver until the afternoon. Janet has Miss Kelly and is on afternoon sessions, and Ann Marie's not home. Oh, it's going to be a long, long morning.

I say to God, please, please, please, one hundred times, please let Rose be in my room. I will study hard. I will try not to talk. I will hang up my clothes and make my bed and help my mother around the house. Please, please, please, I beg.

I go outside and play "Rose is, Rose isn't," pulling the petals off the daisies in my mother's garden. I think how awful it's going to be if Rose isn't in my room and if I'm the only one who has Mr. O'Neil. Who is Mr. O'Neil anyway?

I phone Rose.

"What are you doing?"

"Nothing."

"Want to meet halfway?"

"Why don't you come here. I want to be here when the mailman comes."

I ride my bike to Rose's because it's faster than walking, even though I have to walk the bike up the hill and even though it's still hot enough to fry an egg on the sidewalk. I'm almost at her house, just past Tower Hill School, when I see her running toward me. She's smiling, and she's waving a piece of paper. I don't care how hot it is, I pump as fast as I can. I know she has Mr. O'Neil, too, but I want to see the letter to be sure.

It's the same letter I got. Only it says, "Dear Mr. and Mrs. Jablonski," instead of "Dear Mr. and Mrs. Curtin." Thank you, thank you, thank you, God, I think, so loud I know God can hear me all the way up in Heaven. I didn't mind not having Rose in my room in fifth grade because she was right there, in the room under us. I saw her at recess and at lunch and every day after school. But this year I wouldn't have seen her at all. I park my bike at her house, and we walk all the way to the Dairy Queen to celebrate. Then, because we're so close to St. Bernadette's we stop at church and light a candle. I say thank you, God, again. Then we ring the bell at the rectory and tell Father Finn the good news.

●　●　●　●

I have another reason to light a candle. I'm not supposed to tell anyone, not even Rose. It's a big secret. I crossed my heart and hoped to die before Mama told me. She doesn't want anyone to know. It's too soon, she says. Mama is going to have a baby.

We're in the car, and it's night and dark. The windows are up because it's chilly, though it's still summer. I'm in the back seat, and I have been at Aunt Lorraine's playing with Darlene while my mother and father ran an errand. That's what they told me. But now Mama is telling me that she was at Dr. McSweeney's and that he is very, very hopeful this time.

I know that Mama isn't kidding, but I think, is this true? I hear the words, but they're like words in a story. It's like they're not about me and Mama, but about someone else I don't really know.

Dr. Thompson is our doctor now. I wonder why Mama didn't go to him? Could it be that after all the wishing on stars and wishbones, I might get a little sister or brother, after all?

Gregory Campbell used to be an only child until Leslie

was born. Now there are two of them, and people don't say, when Gregory does something wrong, like forget to put his napkin on his lap or say "God bless you" when someone sneezes, "Oh, he's an only child."

I want to ask Mama when she's having a baby, how long I have to keep this secret and if Lorraine knows, but Mama is talking to my father, and it's as if she's forgotten I'm here. She isn't sitting next to the door the way she always does. She's in the middle of the car. Her head is resting on my father's shoulder, and he has his arm around her.

I think that Mama seems sad, even though she has told me such happy news. I think it's strange that my parents are whispering, not shouting, not excited — like when my father's bank gets full, and he empties all the change onto the bed and yells, "We're millionaires!"

I feel like a millionaire because I'm almost a sister. I wonder what it will be like to be a sister, how having a sister feels. Will I like this baby more than I like Rose, Darlene or Aunt Lorraine? Where will the baby sleep? I want to ask Mama, but I don't, because she has her eyes closed, and my father is talking to her in a soft voice.

Later, I hear more soft voices. My father's. Aunt Lorraine's. Mama's. She had a boy baby once. That's what they whisper. His name was Joseph. He was baptized. They buried him in a cemetery.

When was he born? How old was I?

I can't ask these things because I'm not supposed to be listening.

My mother whispers on the phone to Aunt Lorraine. She tells Lorraine everything. The boy baby had black, curly hair. He looked like my father. She held him before he died. She talks to Lorraine the way I talk to Rose. I wish I could talk to Rose now.

I go to church and light a candle in front of the statue of the Blessed Virgin, and I talk to her: "Your boy died, too. Please watch over my mother. Please ask your son to let her have another boy baby."

Then I go home, and I listen some more. My mother sings in the kitchen, whispers on the phone and laughs, even when what my father says isn't funny. I don't tell Rose that my mother is having a baby. I don't tell Father Finn. I don't even tell Aunt Lorraine that I know what she knows because this is the most important secret I've ever had to keep.

This is the Life

*A*nn Marie knocks on my door and says, "Want to come to the cottage with me?" And I am so excited because Janet, Judy, Chickey and Michelle have all gone to the cottage this summer, and I haven't. I thought Ann Marie didn't like me anymore.

Mama says, "I don't want you going to the cottage all by yourself." But I say, "I'm not going by myself. Mr. and Mrs. Tantillo are going, too. They'll make sure I don't drown."

So my mother calls Mrs. Tantillo and when she hangs up says, "OK, you can go. But I want you to be very careful and not go in the water over your waist because you don't know how to swim. Promise?"

"I promise, Mama."

I don't have to pack a lunch because Ann Marie says there's food at the cottage. I'll get to meet her cousins, she tells me, because they'll be at the cottage, too. We'll all play horseshoes and then swim out to the raft. It's going to be a great day.

Ann Marie says it's a long drive to the cottage but it doesn't feel long. Ann Marie talks so much about the place that I can see it in my head even before we get there.

It isn't at all like what I imagine. Ann Marie's cottage is exactly like the place where my father and I planted the peach trees when I was small. It smells like pine needles, and it feels cool, like standing in front of an open refrigerator door. But there are lots of people at this place; it's not a secret place like my father's and mine. There are tons of kids, and it's so noisy that it sounds like a carnival.

I change into my bathing suit, and from the bathroom window I hear the ping, ping of horseshoes. I haven't played horseshoes since the day I planted the tree with my father. I can't wait to play. But we have to have lunch first, Mrs. Tantillo says.

I'm not very good at horseshoes, so Mr. Tantillo shows me how to hold the heavy upside down U and how to throw it up in the air so that it lands down on the ground near the iron stake that it's supposed to lasso. He does this a few times, and his horseshoes come close. Then he says, "Now you try." I do, and my horseshoe comes even closer.

"Are you sure you don't play this all the time?" Mr. Tantillo says, and I think he is so nice because he didn't say, "Oh, you just got lucky."

I throw a second horseshoe. It lands in the dirt in front of the stake, but close enough so that it makes a ping. Mr. Tantillo and I play horseshoes until Ann Marie says, "Come on, Dad. It's time to go swimming now." Then we all run down to the pond.

Mr. Tantillo, Ann Marie, Claire and Tommy dive right into the water, getting even the tops of their heads wet. I walk in slowly because I don't know how to swim. Ann Marie, Claire and Tommy swim out to the raft where all the kids are jumping off and on. I wish I could swim out to the raft, too.

Mr. Tantillo says, "All you have to do is move your arms like this and kick like this, and that's swimming." He shows me, and I do what he does. Then he says, "If you want to go out to the raft, I'll swim right next to you. But you need to practice where you can touch for a long time before you go over your head by yourself. If I'm beside you, that's different."

I'm scared to even try to swim to the raft because my mother said, "Don't go over your waist," and that raft is way, way over my waist. But Mr. Tantillo is right next to me, and I know that if I sink, he'll save me. It's just that I promised Mama that I wouldn't.

"You don't have to go out there," Mr. Tantillo says.

"No, I want to," I tell him.

So I put my face in the water, kick, move my arms and follow him, and I'm not scared at all. In no time I'm out on the raft with everyone else.

I don't dive off the raft like all the other kids do,

though. I sit and watch. Mr. Tantillo stays in the water and plays with Tommy and Claire. I never knew Mr. Tantillo was so nice. I don't go over Ann Marie's nearly as often as I go over Rosemary's or Janet's. But I think if Mr. Tantillo is always like this, then he's almost as nice as my father.

I sit on the raft until the sun's no longer on my back. Then it gets cold suddenly. It's like an alarm went off. All the kids start diving off the raft and swimming back to the shore. Mr. Tantillo waits until everyone is ahead of us. Then he says, "OK, let's go have dinner," and I slip into the water and kick along beside him.

The Stork Club

*M*ama sleeps a lot: before work, after work and on her days off. I am quiet. I don't bother her.

She sleeps, my father studies, and I dream about what it will be like to have a baby in the house. I will feed the baby when she's hungry, pick her up when she cries and walk her around the block every day. I will take her to the bakery when she's bigger and buy her corn toasties and wipe her hands and her mouth with soft tissue that I will carry in my pocket especially for her. I will hold her hand on the library steps, lead her into the children's room and let her pick out books with big letters and bright pictures. I will read her these books at night, after her bath, when her hair is wet at the ends and she smells like baby powder.

We will go to the movies together, and after the movies I will help her onto the high stool at the soda fountain at the Rexall drug. I will get a lime rickey with two straws and share it with her. Then we will go home.

Mama comes home from work with a bag full of presents for the baby: three tiny T-shirts, a package of diapers and the littlest nightgown I have ever seen. My father stops studying and walks down the stairs. Mama says, "See, Larry. Aren't these the cutest things?" She folds them neatly and puts them on the bottom shelf of the dining room hutch, then steps back and looks at them. He puts his arm around her, and they both smile.

Then Mama says, "I'm going to make dinner now."

"Aren't you going to rest today?" I ask.

"I'm not tired, Baybo. I feel wonderful. Want to help me set the table?"

"Can I tell about the baby now, Mama?"

"Not yet," she says.

"When can I tell?"

"Soon," she says. "Very soon."

Strike It Rich

I start sixth grade. It's the best. We get out at 12:30, so we have the whole afternoon to do anything we want. Plus, Mr. O'Neil is so handsome that Rose and I made up a song about him: "Mr. O'Neil is a guy who could steal, any heart, any place, any time." Mr. O'Neil, William Francis O'Neil, has dark, wavy hair, brown eyes and the best voice. When he sings "Oh, what a beautiful morning," which he does after we say the "Pledge of Allegiance," you would think John Raitt was in the room. He struts as he sings, too, like an actor on a stage, not like a teacher in front of a class.

Michael Ryan, who sits beside me, laughs when Mr. O'Neil sings. I think he's jealous because he wishes that he had a voice like Mr. O'Neil's. He says that he's not jealous and that he's not laughing and that I should mind my own business.

The other good thing about sixth grade is that there are new kids in our room. One of them, Diane Hyman, is really nice. She lives in a new house down at the end of Althea Road, where there used to be all woods, but where now there are two other roads. Diane lives on Smith Road in a house where you can put garbage down the sink. You just stick it in the hole and flick a switch, and the garbage gets chopped up and disappears.

Diane eats blueberries and sour cream. No one makes her eat this, she likes blueberries and sour cream. I don't know what sour cream tastes like, but it looks terrible. Diane says I should try it, that you can't tell if you like something just by looking at it. But I tell her I can.

Diane sits in the front of the room. Rosemary and I sit way in the back. I'm in the second row, and Rose is in the fourth. Debbie Barnes sits between us in row three.

All day, Rose and I write notes back and forth, because we can't just lean over and whisper. Sometimes, Debbie sighs and rolls her eyes when we hand her a note. But she always passes them along, and she never opens them and reads them.

We have music on Thursdays, and we're learning the best cowboy song. It's in two parts. Half the room begins. Then the other half of the room follows.

"It was in the year"
"It was in the year"
"Of '83"
"Of '83"
"That A.J. Stin"
"That A.J. Stin"
"Son hired me"
"Son hired me"
"He said, 'young man"
"He said, 'young man"
" 'I want you to go"
" 'I want you to go"
" 'And drive this herd"
" 'And drive this herd"
"To Mexico.' "
"To Mexico.' "

It sounds great when Mr. O'Neil sings along and when the music teacher makes horse clomping sounds with two sticks and a drum she brings with her.

The mornings go by so fast. We don't eat lunch at school, but Mr. O'Neil lets us have a snack at eleven o'clock. Rosemary's mother always packs Rose's snacks in aluminum foil, instead of in ordinary wax paper. I think her snacks taste better because of this.

I'm reading "Heidi," and I love it. I have to do a book report, and I don't even mind because it's the best book I've ever read. I think Heidi is so lucky to have a friend like Peter, but it's so sad that she has to leave him and move to the city. I would hate to move to the city and leave Rosemary.

"Someday, when I grow up, I'm going to write a book like 'Heidi,' " I tell Rose. She says I can't do this because I don't know anything about Switzerland or goats.

• • • •

We get a new car, a 1957 Chevy Impala. "It's a real new car, fresh from the factory, the first new car I've ever owned," my father says.

My mother gets a mink stole. A stole is like a cape that you wear to keep your shoulders warm. All the movie stars have them and wear them to parties. My mother wears her mink stole to church.

I ask Mama, "Did your ship come in?" She smiles and says, "Well, not the big ship. That's still out there. But a little one did."

I didn't know Mama had more than one ship out on the ocean. I wonder how you get ships full of wonderful things like new cars and mink stoles, why it is that some people have ships and some people don't, and if I'll have ships when I'm grown-up.

The Russians launched a satellite, which is orbiting the earth like a tiny moon. Everyone — parents, teachers, kids and even Father Finn and Father Kelleher — has been talking about it. Mr. O'Neil says the Russians are way ahead of us in the race for space. Rosemary nodded her head when he said this; she knows all about these things. Last year, Mr. Holmes taught science for a whole hour every day. He was always standing on a chair pretending he was an atom or a planet or something, showing, not just telling his class about the way the world works. Because of Mr. Holmes, Rosemary knows the names of the stars and the planets and all about things like the speeds of light and sound.

Mr. O'Neil knows a lot about science, too, and says that outer space is the next frontier.

My father tells my mother that you can't trust those Russians and that Sputnik might be some secret spy device. He says Russia doesn't care about outer space at all; it just wants to take over the world, close all the churches and make kids spy on their parents. I think Sputnik might drop a bomb on us like in "The Day the World Ended." Rose says, "Beverly, this has nothing to do with that," and, because she knows that Jupiter has moons around it, I believe her.

• • • •

My father comes home from work with four tickets to the policeman's ball, not just two, and he says that I can go and that I can invite Rosemary if I want.

If I want? The policeman's ball is a big, huge party where ladies wear gowns and white gloves and men wear tuxedos and shiny shoes. Kids usually don't go at all. But my father says I can go because this year's ball is at Symphony Hall — a beautiful old building in Boston where orchestras play and rich people go to listen — and that it's a once-in-a-lifetime opportunity for me to experience this place.

"Are we rich, Dad, now that our ship has come in? Is this why I can go to the ball, too?"

"No. We're not rich. But for a night we can pretend that we are."

The only bad thing is I that have to wear an ugly, see-through, white organza, sleeveless dress with red polka dots that Mama bought me. I hate this dress, but she says it's pretty and it looks nice on me, and that's that.

But it isn't pretty. I wear three full-length crinolines under it, and you can still see my bra. I borrow two more crinolines from Rose, and I think you can still see the bra straps, but Rose says you can't. Mama says, "You are not wearing five slips under that dress, Beverly. That's ridiculous."

"But I have to, Mama, or I don't want to go to the ball."

Mama sighs. She tells me that it's perfectly natural to have breasts and that someday I'll be glad I have them.

But I'm not glad. Rosemary looks so pretty in her lavender organza dress. I wish I looked like Rose. Her chest doesn't stick out, her arms aren't fat and ugly and she isn't turning round everywhere.

The night of the ball, I wear a white, button-down sweater over my dress. It's Rose's sweater. I tell Mama,

"I'm cold. I think I'm getting sick." She puts her hand on my forehead and looks in my eyes.

"Wear the sweater, if it makes you feel better," my mother says.

Symphony Hall is like a cathedral, it's so pretty, but it's even bigger, with a lot more statues and chandeliers. It's fun to watch all the pretty people dancing. My father dances with Rose, then with me. But we don't know how to dance, not the right way, so we decide to walk around and explore instead. We climb the stairs to the balcony above the dance floor and look down at everyone. It's like looking into a fairy tale full of kings and queens.

Halfway through the night, a girl a little older than we are comes on the stage. The orchestra leader introduces her as someone's daughter. Then he says she is going to sing some song I don't know. She stands in front of the microphone, and the orchestra plays. It sounds just like Lawrence Welk, and she sings and sounds like Janet Lennon. No one is dancing anymore. Everyone is looking at her. I say, "I want to sing, too. Do you want to sing, Rose?"

"What could we sing?"

" 'Tammy.' I could sing the first verse, and you could sing the second, just like in our Minstrel Show. Let's do it. Let's go down there now."

We race down the steps across the hall and up to the orchestra leader. We say, together, as if we'd planned it, "We can sing, too. We can sing, 'Tammy.' " And the nice man with the baton says, "OK, girls. When she's finished it will be your turn."

Everyone is looking at us as we climb up on the stage. I have to begin. I wish Rose were singing first. I wish we were singing together, but it's too late now. The orchestra is playing, and it's time for me to start.

I look out at the dance hall full of people, and for just a second, I want to run off the stage and out the door all the way home and hide under my bed. But then I think

I'm Debbie Reynolds, and right outside my window is a beautiful summer night. A soft breeze is cooling me and making the curtains flap, and I'm in love with someone who looks like George Falcone. I sing, "I hear the cotton wood, whisperin' above, Tammy, Tammy, Tammy's in love" and I forget there are people watching me.

When the audience claps I'm surprised because, though I'm finished singing, it's the middle of the song. Then the band stops. Now I'm really confused because it's Rose's turn, don't they know?

The man with the baton looks at us. I say, "It's her turn," and everyone hears because the microphone is on. The audience claps again, and the orchestra starts up. Rose sings the second verse, and everyone gets quiet because her voice is so beautiful.

Later, people we don't know tell us, "You did a wonderful job, girls. See you in Hollywood. Hey, are you Patience and Prudence?" I know they're only being nice, but the words make us feel good anyway.

Rosemary sleeps at my house, and morning comes quickly. We don't wash our faces before school because the pink lipstick we were allowed to wear "just this once," which we reapplied before we went to bed, is still on and we don't want to smudge it. I ask Rose if she wants to wear my white dress with the red polka dots to school, so I can wear her purple one. She shrugs, which means OK. So we swap dresses, go downstairs, eat breakfast and take the bus to school.

Mr. O'Neil says, "Do you want to tell the class about last night?" So we do. We don't stand in the front of the class, though. We sit at our seats and talk and answer questions.

Later, after school, as we are walking down the hall to leave, Miss Kelly, the other sixth-grade teacher who has afternoon sessions, sees us in our fancy party dresses and says, "Where are you girls off to?"

Rose says, "We went to the policeman's ball at Symphony Hall last night, Miss Kelly. Beverly's father is a policeman. We wore our dresses today just for fun."

"Well, that dress is certainly very becoming on you, Rosemary. Your mother has excellent taste."

And then Miss Kelly says, "Enjoy the rest of the after-noon, girls," and walks away.

Me wearing Rosemary's dress

A Guest in Your Home

All the kids go ice skating on the pond behind the School for the Deaf. I don't have ice skates, so I can't go.

"I wish I could go ice skating with Janet and Ann Marie," I tell Mama.

"Maybe you should ask Santa for ice skates for Christmas," she says.

I am in sixth grade. I wear a bra. I am so grown-up that Rose and I have even figured out how you get a baby. If a man sees you naked, then God gives you a baby. That's why in the magazines her father keeps hidden under his mattress, the naked girls are always wearing something, like a rose, a tattoo or false eyelashes. They can't get totally naked because then they would get pregnant, Rose says.

I wonder how can we be so smart and know all this and not know if there's a Santa Claus. Rose insists there is absolutely, definitely no real Santa, that he's just a man in a red suit. And I think there's probably not a real Santa, too, because how can one person deliver presents to every child in the world in a single night? But my mother says, "Of course, there's a Santa Claus, Beverly. Do you think I would lie to you?"

So I'm still not sure.

• • • •

Mama is in the kitchen at the table drinking coffee and talking to Vera Campbell and Virginia Minetolli when my friend comes to visit. I go to use the bathroom, and there it is, just like Mama said. I'm not scared or upset because this is natural; this is what happens to girls when they're growing up.

I do exactly what Mama told me to do. I come out of the bathroom and walk over to her and say, "Excuse me for interrupting." Then, using our secret language, I announce, "Mama, my friend has come to visit."

Vera Campbell practically falls off her chair. "Oh my God, you've got your period. You're so young, but isn't this a momentous occasion." Mama jumps up, and hugs me and starts to cry. Virginia Minetolli, who got her finger chopped off by an electric mixer when she was making a birthday cake for her daughter Louise, sits and looks at me.

I dart back into the bathroom, slam the door and cry. Now everyone knows what was supposed to be a secret. What did I do wrong? Why did they know what I was talking about?

My father must hear the commotion from upstairs where he's studying because he comes running down into the kitchen where there is sudden quiet, then whispering. Now my father knows, too.

Mama knocks on the bathroom door, opens it, comes in and puts her arms around me. "It's OK. It's my fault. My mother told me it was a secret language, Beverly. I thought it was. I didn't know. I'm so sorry."

Vera Campbell and Virginia Minetolli are gone when I come out of the bathroom. My father is at the stove frying bologna, my favorite thing. He smiles at me and hands me a piece of bologna straight from the pan.

The next day at the bus stop no one says a thing to me about a period at the end of a sentence or about a friend coming to visit. Gregory Campbell doesn't look at me funny. Michael Ryan doesn't stare. The whole world doesn't know. Not even Rose knows. I don't tell anyone that my friend has come to visit.

Rose comes over to my house to help trim our Christmas tree because we put ours up way earlier than everyone. My father loves decorating the tree. He strings the lights and hangs the Styrofoam balls covered with sequins that my mother and I made on the branches that Rose and I can't reach. Then we do the rest.

Rose and I try to take the wrinkles out of the tinsel because unwrinkled tinsel looks shinier on the tree. This is hard to do because it keeps breaking, so after a while we stop and use the tinsel as it is.

Mama comes into the parlor and exclaims, "Larry, you did it again," and "Girls, you did a wonderful job!" Then we have eggnog, shut off the lights, sit on the couch and admire the tree.

Later I tell Mama that Rose is so lucky at Christmas because she has a million relatives and they all send her sweaters, pajamas, books and games. We don't have any relatives, except for the Nanas and Aunt Lorraine.

"How come Uncle Leroy, Jimmy, Billy and Buddy don't send me Christmas presents?" I ask Mama. She says, "Because we don't send their children gifts."

"Why don't we, Mama?"

"Because we're not very close, I guess."

"Some of Rosemary's aunts and uncles aren't close either, but they mail her gifts."

"I didn't mean close like that. I meant close as a family," my mother says.

I wonder why we're not close as a family. Once in a while Uncle Leroy comes to visit with Donna, his daughter, and they're really nice. They stay and have supper, and everyone seems close. Uncle Jimmy came a long time ago with Fran and their son, Sandy. My Uncle Buddy stopped by when I was small and hugged me and lifted me up high and twirled me around. I liked him, and I know he liked me.

But except for Leroy, they live far away, and Mama says when years go by and you don't see people, you grow apart.

Like when Jeannie Sullivan moved, I think. I hope I never move. I would hate to grow apart from Rose.

Stop the Music

My mother is in the hospital, and my father is on the phone. "This is the last time," he is saying to Little Nana, or maybe it's Aunt Lorraine he's talking to. I don't know. He doesn't tell me, and I don't ask.

I feed Shane and sit outside on the back steps and watch him eat. He wags his tail as he chews. My father hangs up the phone and shouts from inside. "Mrs. Tantillo invited you for dinner."

Why would Mrs. Tantillo do this? I've never eaten at her house before, not dinner anyway. Cookies, sometimes, if I'm over there, and Ann Marie wants one. "I don't want to go to Mrs. Tantillo's for dinner, Dad. I want to go to Rosemary's or stay home."

But there's no talking to my father. He can't be worried about me, he says. That's the last thing he needs right now. "Just be a good girl and do what I tell you, OK?"

I walk over to Mrs. Tantillo's, and she's in the kitchen making spaghetti sauce. Claire, Tommy and Ann Marie are at the kitchen table doing their homework. Everyone is quiet and serious.

We are going to eat in the dining room. I wonder if the Tantillos eat in the dining room every night. I want to ask Ann Marie, but I can't because her mother's right here. I hope we're not eating in the dining room because of me.

When Mr. Tantillo comes home from work, he doesn't act surprised to see me at the kitchen table doing my homework. He doesn't say, when dinner is ready, "It's time for you to go home, Beverly." I think he must know that my mother is sick and in the hospital. I think they must all know. But how? And if they do, do they know why she is there?

I wish I could ask where the hospital is, how long my mother will be away and if this means that there won't be a baby, again. But I can't — no one's supposed to know about the baby. The baby is a secret that I can't tell.

The table looks so pretty. There's a big bowl of spaghetti and another bowl of red sauce. There are meatballs, sausages and a basket of fresh bread. There's margarine in a tub, not butter on a plate like at my house, and a can of grated cheese.

My mother never makes this kind of spaghetti. She fries onions and hamburger in a pan, boils elbows in another pan, opens a can of sauce, mixes the whole thing together and puts it in one bowl on the kitchen table. I love my mother's spaghetti.

I am very careful when I take Mrs. Tantillo's spaghetti from the bowl and put it on my plate. I don't want to spill anything on her pretty tablecloth. I am especially careful with the red sauce and take just a little. When the meatballs are handed to me I take two, because I'm starving and I love meatballs. I don't take any sausages because they don't look like the kind my mother makes.

I butter the bread, and it's so easy to do because the margarine is soft. I take a big bite, and it's delicious. Then I pick up my fork and cut into my meatball. I'm about to tell Mrs. Tantillo how good the meatball is, but when I look up, everyone is staring at me. "In our house we say grace before we eat," Mrs. Tantillo says. "Tommy, I think it's your turn."

I put down my fork, stop chewing and let the meatball sit in the corner of my mouth as I mumble, "Bless us, O Lord, and these thy gifts, which we are about to receive from thy bounty, through Christ, Our Lord, Amen." I can feel my face turning red.

After grace, there is silence. Then Tommy starts to laugh, and Mrs. Tantillo says, "That's not nice, Tommy." Then everyone says, "Pass the meatballs. Pass the sausages. I'll have some bread down here."

I should have known better than to start eating first. I should have thought about grace. Why didn't I? Now Mrs. Tantillo is thinking that she has three polite children and that my mother has only one child, and look what a bad job she's done with just one child. Now Mrs. Tantillo thinks that I'm rude as well as spoiled.

I can hardly swallow my meatballs. I want to go home, but I can't go anywhere. I have to stay here and pretend that I don't know what Mrs. Tantillo is thinking.

Mr. Tantillo picks up his fork and spoon and says, "I bet you never saw a real Italian eat spaghetti before, huh?" Then he twirls the spaghetti onto the fork, but using his spoon, too, and puts the neat ball of spaghetti in his mouth.

"What do you think of that? Want to try it? It's easy."

Mr. Tantillo is right. It is easy. I twirl and eat, twirl and eat, and I don't have to look at anyone or talk to anyone because I'm so busy doing this.

After dinner they offer dessert — it's ice cream. I say, "No, thank you," because I know I'll spill it. I offer to help with the dishes, but Mrs. Tantillo says, "No, you two girls go on and finish your homework."

"I'm finished," I tell Mrs. Tantillo. "I'd like to help."

"No, no. That's OK, dear. Why don't you and Ann Marie play a game."

We play gin rummy for a long time until my father finally comes and gets me. I say, "Thank you very much," to Mrs. Tantillo, and she says, "You're welcome, Beverly." My father drives to our house in silence. Then he sits in our driveway, his hands on the steering wheel. He doesn't shut off the car. He looks like he's forgotten that it's on.

"Your mother won't be home for a couple of days," he finally says.

"Is she OK?" I ask.

He nods, then turns the key and opens the car door.

"And the baby? Is the baby OK, too, Dad?"

My father shakes his head no.

I walk behind him into the house. Shane wags his tail and follows him into his room, but my father isn't noticing Shane either. "I'll let Shane out. Then I'm going to bed, Dad," I say. I wish I knew what else to say.

I kiss my father good night, and his cheek is wet. I

don't understand; I think, why is my father's cheek wet? Then I know. He's crying. My father is crying. I didn't know that fathers cried.

I take care of Shane. Then I walk upstairs and change for bed. I say my prayers. But I don't pray to God to do better than Rosemary on our geography test or to please make my breasts stop growing. I talk to God like He's my friend, like Father Finn says you're supposed to. I say, God, how come Mrs. Tantillo, Mrs. Butler, Mrs. Jablonski and Mrs. Barnes have three children, and my mother has only one? How come Mrs. Lyons and Mrs. DiNatale are always having babies? I say, God, my mother lights candles, goes to church and even has a statue of your Blessed Mother in our back yard. She plants flowers around the statue. She has baby clothes in the hutch, God. Can't you please give her her baby back? You don't have to give her lots of babies. Just this one. This would be enough. If you do this, God, I swear I won't ever ask for anything ever again.

Please, I say, please, not just a hundred times, but over and over. I say, please, God, please, even in my dreams.

Lights Out

*M*ama comes home and sleeps and sleeps. Sometimes when I get home from school, she's still sleeping.

"Mama, it's one o'clock," I say.

"Is it that late already?"

She gets up and makes toast, bacon and hot coffee. We sit at the table, and Mama smokes her cigarettes while I eat. She picks at the food on her plate. She looks tired, even though she sleeps all the time.

Aunt Lorraine comes to visit with Darlene. She makes Mama laugh. She tells funny stories about Big Nana and people she and Mama knew when they were growing up. Janet Butler makes Mama laugh, too. She comes over, knocks on our door and says, "Hi-O-Beverly, are you coming out to play?"

We're having chicken soup. My mother made it. "Would you like some?" she asks Janet.

Janet says, "Yes, please." She comes in, sits down, eats a whole bowl of soup, then clutches her stomach, pretends she is dying and sings in a dramatic voice, "I'll die tomorrow."

Janet is in a singing mood. Sometimes she does this. She'll sing everything instead of saying it. It makes everyone laugh, even Mama.

"Why don't you and Janet take Darlene for a walk around the block," Lorraine says, after Janet eats another bowl of soup. Janet and I love to take Darlene out because we can make her say anything. She's like a parrot. "Say sky, Darlene," and she'll repeat in her high little voice, "Sky."

"Say banana," I tell her.

"Banana," Darlene says.

"Hippopotamus," Janet says.

"Hippopotamus," Darlene repeats.

"Say Janet loves George," I tell her.

"Janet loves George," Darlene chimes.

All the way around the block, we tell Darlene to say

things, and she does. She's so serious and concentrates so hard that it makes us laugh.

We sing to Darlene, too, and she sings back. I'm teaching her "Oh be careful little eyes what you see."

I wish Aunt Lorraine would come and live with us again. Every time Lorraine is with Mama, Mama is happy. But when Lorraine leaves, Mama gets sad again.

I hear her talking to my father about foster children. "What are foster children?" I ask them.

My father says that foster children are children whose parents aren't able to take care of them for a while. So they stay in other people's homes until their parents can take care of them.

"Then what happens?"

"Then they go back to their parents."

My father tells my mother that taking in a foster child is a bad idea. "Think how you'd feel, Dot, if you took care of a baby for six months, a year, two years, and then one day someone knocked on the door and said, 'OK, you have to give the baby back.' You think you're broken-hearted now? You'd be a lot more brokenhearted then."

Mama sighs. "No, I wouldn't be, Larry. Can't we at least look into it? Sometimes they let you adopt foster children, don't they?"

"See, you're already doing it. You already want to keep a baby you've never even seen. It's too much, Dot. I'm not going to let you talk me into this. I'm not going to do this. This is the end of it. It's over."

Then my father marches upstairs to study.

I sit at the table with my mother. I wonder what happened to the baby clothes that were in the hutch in the dining room. I wonder why God didn't answer my prayers.

The Littlest Angel

*R*ose invites me to a Christmas party at her church. "Can I go?" I ask Mama.

I'm not supposed to go to Rosemary's church. It's OK for her to come to mine, but it's a sin if I go to hers. That's the rule.

But Mama says, "I don't think God would mind if you went to a Christmas party with Rose."

I wear my red and white polka-dotted dress because, with Rose's sweater, I don't hate it as much. Rose wears her purple dress again. Even Mr. and Mrs. Jablonski get dressed up.

I've never seen them dressed for a party. Mrs. Jablonski is always in a house coat, and Mr. Jablonski is always in his work clothes, khaki pants and a T-shirt. But tonight he has on a jacket and tie, and Mrs. Jablonski is wearing a navy blue dress and pearls. They both look real nice.

Rosemary's church party is so much fun. First we eat dinner at big, long tables — turkey, mashed potatoes and cranberry sauce — then we have apple pie and ice cream. Then Santa comes, and the little kids sit on his lap. Then we get to watch a movie called "The Littlest Angel."

It is the saddest story about a small angel who doesn't fit in anywhere, is always getting into trouble and is always doing the wrong thing. But then he does a very wonderful thing, and you know, after that, he fits in just fine, though the movie doesn't show this.

When the movie ends, we sing Christmas songs: "Frosty" and "Santa Claus Is Coming to Town." We sing hymns, too, not just the first verse, but all the verses. We get candy canes to take home and coloring books if we want. Rose and I don't take them, though. We're too old for coloring books, we say. But I wish we weren't too old, because I love to color.

I sleep over at Rose's house. I change into her ski pajamas, and she wears my red plaid pajamas. We brush our teeth side by side in her big bathroom with the white tile floor. Then we run into her room because the floor is cold on our bare feet. We jump into her bed and pull the covers up to our necks. We continue singing Christmas hymns until Mrs. Jablonski knocks on the door, opens it and says, "You girls should try to get some sleep. You'll never get up for school in the morning."

So we sing in softer voices. We sing every song we know, and when we're finished, we talk in whispers.

I wish I could tell Rose about the baby. I wish I could tell her that I think I have a sister or a brother who is just like the littlest angel living up in Heaven and that I know how he feels. I wish I could talk to her about foster children, my father's wet cheeks and all the pleases I said to God that he didn't hear.

But though I tell Rosemary everything, I know that this isn't mine to tell. And so I say, "Good night, Rose" and she says, "Good night, Bev," and we turn on our sides and go to sleep.

• • • •

It's Christmas eve, and Mama is basting the turkey. Big Nana is sitting at the kitchen table sipping port wine and telling Mama what she thinks is the best way to cook turkey. Little Nana is telling Big Nana that Dorothy's turkeys are always moist, not like the kind she used to cook when her boys were small, turkeys so dry they would unstick her false teeth.

Little Nana is always unsticking her false teeth. She does this to make me laugh. She'll be in the middle of a serious story, and all of a sudden, her teeth will be sitting outside her lips.

"I don't know why you do that, Kay," Big Nana says this night, as Little Nana's teeth hang below her bottom lip. But I know why. Little Nana does it for me.

My father drove to Cambridge and picked up the Nanas. He does this every Christmas eve. Big Nana always has to work late, so he doesn't get home until almost midnight. Mama says that Big Nana doesn't have to work late on Christmas eve, that she chooses to do this. Mama says it would be a lot easier for everyone if Big Nana could leave work at a decent hour and not arrive at our house when every other family is already in bed.

But I love staying up late, sitting at the kitchen table with the Nanas, sipping wine, smelling the turkey that Mama cooks slowly all night long. I like Christmas eve even more than I like Christmas day because Little Nana always says, "Why don't you open my present before you go to bed, Beverly." Then my father says, "Well, you may as well open one of the presents your mother and I got you," because my father works early on Christmas morning and if I don't open it now I'll have to wait until Christmas afternoon.

I open these presents in the parlor by the light of the tree. Everything else is dark, outside and inside. It's like a magic time. I give the Nanas their presents, cards I made, then my mother and father exchange presents. We don't go to bed until after three in the morning.

I don't hear my father leave for work the next morning. I wake to the sounds of my mother clinking dishes in the kitchen.

The Nanas are already at the table drinking tea and eating Irish bread. The room is bright now, and the turkey is on top of the stove. But it's like nothing has really changed from the night before — except now it's Christmas day.

Rose calls and tells me all the presents she got: skirts and sweaters, an eight-ball and a Monopoly game. I tell her I haven't opened my presents yet, that I just got up. She says, "You just got up?"

There is a present wrapped in plain brown paper under the tree that has my name on it. "What's this?" I ask my mother. She says, "It's a gift from Uncle Buddy."

Buddy is my uncle who lives in California. He's never sent me a present before, not in my whole, entire life. "Did you tell him to send me this?" I ask Mama.

"No, I didn't," she says. "It came in the mail. I couldn't believe it either. Open it, and let's see what it is."

It's a very long, rectangular box, and I can't even imagine what it is because Uncle Buddy doesn't know me and hasn't seen me since he picked me up and twirled me over his head. There's a note taped to the box.

"To Beverly. I saw this and thought of you. Love, Uncle Buddy."

I open the box and pull back the tissue paper, and two blue eyes are staring at me. "It's a doll, Mama. He sent me a doll."

But it isn't just any old doll, it's the most beautiful doll I've ever seen. She has dark blond, curly hair, a black velvet jacket, a red plaid skirt, long white socks and black shiny shoes. And, this doll walks! Not pretend walks with me helping her, like some of my dolls. She really walks. There's a hole in her back that a key fits in. I wind her up and take her into the kitchen, and she makes a buzzing sound as she struts across the linoleum floor, her arms and legs stiff, like a toy soldier's.

"I saw this and thought of you," Uncle Buddy wrote. I wonder why. I think it's kind of funny that he was thinking of me when I was thinking of him.

Mama says, "I've never seen a doll like this in my entire life." Mama winds her up, and she marches, this time toward the back door, where Shane is lying. He barks at her, and when she doesn't stop walking, he gets up and moves.

I open all my other presents. In the afternoon Aunt Lorraine and Uncle Frank come over, and there are more gifts to open. I like everything.

But Christmas night, when I'm lying in my bed thinking about the day, I know that even though I like almost everything I got, it's the doll my Uncle Buddy sent that I like best of all.

Press Conference

*A*fternoon sessions are even better than morning sessions, because now I can watch old movies before I go to school. The whole movie isn't shown at once. You get to see a little every day for five days. On Mondays, the movies begin. On Fridays, they end. "And now for the conclusion," the announcer always says.

This week I'm watching "Humoresque," a story about a man who plays a violin. It stars John Garfield, who is very handsome and who is my favorite actor, even though he's dead. I love the music in this movie. I never noticed before how sad a violin can make you feel. Sometimes it sounds as if the violin is crying.

Rose is watching "Humoresque" at her house, too. Mama says she wishes that she could sit and watch it, but she can't because she'd be late for work. Mama is working at Wethern's again, because Mr. Rich called and said he needed her.

After the movie is over, I read. This week I'm reading "Paintbox Summer," by Betty Cavanna. It's such a good book that it makes me forget it's winter outside. Here I am sitting in the parlor on the green chair in my long-sleeve sweater and wool skirt, but I'm not really here at all. I'm lying on a blanket on a beach, watching a boat float by, it's hot, and I can hear kids playing around me. It's all so real I think I can feel sand under my toes!

I want to write a book like this when I grow up. I want to write a story that will make people forget where they are.

Mr. O'Neil has taught us a lot about writing stories. He's taught us about similes, metaphors and alliteration. Alliteration is my favorite. "She sells seashells down by the seashore." I also like onomatopoeia. That's when a word sounds like what it means, like growl, buzz and fizzle.

Mr. O'Neil is serious about grammar. Some of it's hard, like when to use who and whom, but most of it's easy.

Rose says we should put our new writing skills to use.

She says, "Why don't we print a newspaper, Bev. We have plenty of time. We can write stuff during the week, print it on Saturday and deliver it on Sunday. We won't charge for a few weeks, and then we will. Then we'll be rich."

Rosemary thinks of everything. She thinks of beginning a paper. She thinks of a great name, *The Weekly Sputnik*. She even knows what we'll need in *The Weekly Sputnik*: a news section, not with news of the world, but with news of the neighborhood and news of the school; a gossip column; an interview section, where we can talk to people like Mr. O'Neil about the things they do; a listing of the movies downtown, because they change on Sunday and Wednesday; and maybe even a book review sometimes. "What do you think, Bev?"

I think that in the whole world there isn't anyone smarter than Rose, and I wonder sometimes why she hangs around with me.

What we need, we decide, to make our newspaper look like a real paper is a printing press. There's one at the five-and-ten, but we don't have the money to buy it. It costs ten dollars, and ten dollars is a fortune. Rose empties her silver pig, and I empty my bank. We count all our change, and we are eight dollars short.

We could write out the papers by hand. It would look nice this way because Rose makes little O's instead of dots over her I's, but she'd have to do all the writing because my R's sometimes look like N's. Mr. O'Neil says it's hard to read my writing, and we don't want to print a paper that people can't read.

"I don't think I could do all the writing," Rose says. "My hand would kill."

We really need a printing press.

On Saturday, we walk to Woolworth's and ask the saleslady to take the printing press from the top shelf where they put all the expensive stuff. We stand and study it through the see-through paper, and it looks perfect. We figure that if we don't go to the movies for sixteen weeks we can get it. We'll just have to save, we decide. If we give up the movies, corn toasties, lime rickeys and Charleston Chews, we can get the printing press in two months! But two months is forever. In two months it will be almost spring. In two months someone else could steal our idea.

"I could sell my Little Lulu comic books and get some money," I say, instantly wishing I hadn't said these words. I want to take them back. I want to say, "I didn't mean that. I was only kidding."

But Rose says, "That's a fantastic idea. I should have thought of it," and I feel good because I thought of it first.

"I'll sell my comic books, too," Rose says. "We're getting too old for comic books anyway."

But I don't feel too old for comic books. I love my Little Lulu comic books. I love Little Lulu, Tubby and Little Itch, and I don't want to sell my comic books. I want to keep them forever. But now I've said it, and Rose thinks it's a great idea. There's no going back.

Ann Marie buys them. The whole bunch. She says, "I can't believe you're selling them, Bev." She hands me a five-dollar bill, and I hand her my entire life's collection. I try not to think about all my Little Lulus sitting over at her house on her bookshelf in her room.

Rose and I pool our money, and we walk down to Woolworth's and buy the printing press. On the way home we stop at Gilroy's, and with our leftover money we buy two cake mixes, two boxes of marshmallow frosting and red sprinkles. It's almost Valentine's Day, and we've decided to make cakes for our mothers.

That was Rose's idea, too. "We'll make heart-shaped cakes and surprise them."

I interview Miss Kelly and Mr. O'Neil for the first issue of *The Weekly Sputnik*. I ask them where they live, how long they have been teachers and what made them decide they wanted to teach.

When Mr. O'Neil says this is his first year teaching, I

can't believe it. And when he says he lives at home with his mother, I can't believe this even more. I write down his address. Then, instead of going home, I walk to Rose's and tell her this. She says, "Let's call information and get his phone number, then call his house."

A woman answers. We hang up. A while later we call again. Mr. O'Neil answers. Rose disguises her voice and asks for Mr. McNeil. Mr. O'Neil says, "I'm sorry. You have the wrong number." Then he hangs up.

I write the interview. Rose writes the gossip story. She writes that Arthur Litchenstein likes Sandra Singer, which isn't big news. Every boy in the school likes Sandra Singer. She just moved to Randolph. She wears tight sweaters and has big breasts, plus she is beautiful. Even the girls can't help looking at her.

We have everything written. On Saturday, we'll print. On Sunday, we'll deliver. In a few weeks, we'll be rich, Rose says. In a few weeks, when I'm rich, the first thing I'm going to do is buy my Little Lulu comic books back.

• • • •

Suddenly, Rose is being weird. She thinks that "he don't" sounds better than "he doesn't," so she's decided to say this from now on. I don't think this is such a great idea, considering we're just days away from going into the publishing business.

"You sound like Stanley Kowalski," I tell her, thinking this will make her stop, because when we saw "A Streetcar Named Desire" we couldn't figure out how anyone in the world could ever like Stanley Kowalski.

But it only makes her worse.

"Grace Winters said she'd come over and help us print the paper on Saturday," Rose says. "But she don't have to if you don't want."

Grace Winters is Rose's friend, not mine, and when Rose says, "Grace is coming, too," or "Grace is stopping by," I sigh and roll my eyes because I wish she weren't.

But what I wish right now has nothing to do with

Grace. I wish Rose would stop saying "he don't" and "she don't" because she's driving me crazy.

"Please stop!" I beg.

"Stop what?"

"Trying to sound stupid."

"I'm not trying to sound stupid. It's stupid to use two syllables when you don't have to."

Rose has an answer for everything.

Grace comes over and helps us print the paper. I'm actually glad to see her because at least she talks like a normal human being.

The printing press is terrible. It hardly works. The tiny rubber letters keep falling off the tiny metal plates, and when you crank the drum, the papers gets stuck and the print blurs. It takes all day to get about ten pages that you can almost read. Rose says, "The first time is always the hardest." I'm so grateful for a grammatically correct sentence that I don't tell her that this is the dumbest thing she's ever said. We've done this at least a hundred times already, and it hasn't gotten a bit easier.

"I'll deliver the papers before church in the morning," I tell Rose. She walks home with Grace. I don't walk them halfway because I don't want to listen to Rose talk. That makes me feel awful because I have never felt this way before.

The paper is not a success. I ask Ann Marie, "What do you think?" She says, "It's OK," and Janet says, "It's hard to read." Chickey Fleming says, "I never got one." I explain that we didn't have enough, but that next week we'll print more.

Only we don't. Next week comes, and the same thing happens, except that Rose isn't saying "he don't" anymore because her mother made her stop, and Grace isn't here to help us. We're alone. We're putting the letters on the press, putting the ink where it belongs, positioning the paper and cranking, but it doesn't work.

We give up. We throw the printing press in the trash.

We have sixty cents between us. We walk downtown and split a corn toastie. Then we walk up the library stairs, return our books, pick out some new ones and spend the rest of our money on the movies.

Tightrope

*I*t's February 13th, the day before Valentine's Day — time to make the Valentine cakes.

Rose comes over before school. My mother and father are at work. We have the house to ourselves. I take out two bowls, two round pans and a measuring cup.

"Don't forget to preheat the oven," Rose says.

We mix the cakes by hand at the kitchen table. It's hard work, mixing, and it's sloppy work, too. Rose says, "Why don't you get the electric mixer?" So I do. The cake batter is light and fluffy as we pour it into the pans.

While our cakes cook we wash the bowls so we can use them for the frosting. I've never seen frosting in a box before. My mother uses confectioners' sugar, a little vanilla, milk and Crisco and whips it all up. Her frosting is delicious, but this is special marshmallow frosting, which Rosemary says is even better.

It's hard to whip this frosting without making a mess. The electric mixer spatters it everywhere. So I get two deeper bowls, wash the other bowls, wipe off the walls, the counter and the floor, and start over.

It takes forever to turn the white liquid into something that looks like marshmallow, but it finally happens. The oven buzzes. Our cakes are done. We turn them upside down and shake them out of the pan. Rose's comes out perfectly. Mine falls apart.

Rose says, "Don't worry, Bev. We can glue it back together with the frosting." The frosting covers all our mistakes, and what the frosting doesn't hide, the red sprinkles do.

We clean up quickly. It's almost noon, and the school bus will be here soon. We have to change because our clothes and even our shoes are sticky.

Rose comes back to my house after school. My father is picking up my mother at work. They'll be home any minute. I hurry and climb to the top cabinet to get some candles. We put them on our cakes, and when the car pulls into the driveway I light them.

"Surprise!" Rose and I yell when my mother opens the door. She stands on the threshold speechless.

When she finally talks, she says, "What have you done!" and she's not smiling. She looks mad, and I don't understand.

"We made Valentine cakes, Mama. One for you and one for Mrs. Jablonski. Do you like them?"

In the flickering candlelight it's hard to see that the two blobs of frosting on the kitchen table are really heart-shaped cakes. So I turn on the overhead light so that my mother can see better.

In that light's sudden glare, I see what she sees. Not just one semi-ugly and one very ugly cake, but a kitchen covered in marshmallow and red sprinkles.

"I can't believe this," my mother says.

She throws her pocketbook on a chair, grabs a towel, puts soap and water on it and begins to scrub the cabinets, the walls and the floor. Rose says, "I think I better go home." My father says, "Give me a minute, and I'll drive you."

Then he puts his hand on my mother's shoulder. "Dot," he says, "They didn't mean it. They were trying to do something nice. They're just kids. They wanted to make you happy. They're not the reason you're mad."

My mother stops scrubbing. She sits on a kitchen chair. Then she sobs like she does at old movies, like she does late at night when my father is working and she thinks I'm asleep.

"I'm sorry," she says. "You're right. It's not them. It's me. They tried hard, and I went and ruined it."

"You didn't ruin it, Dot," my father says. And I say, "You didn't, Mama. Really."

My father walks into the bedroom, gets his camera and takes a picture of the cakes. "Years from now, when we look at this picture we'll all laugh," he says.

My father drives Rose and her cake home. I help Mama clean up the mess. We have hot dogs and beans and my cake for dinner.

When the picture is developed and I see it on my father's new slide projector screen, I am surprised, not because the cakes are even uglier than I remember, but because when I think of those cakes, I picture baby clothes in the hutch behind them.

But the hutch isn't behind them. There's just the dining room wall. That's what's in the picture. A wall.

So why do I look at the picture of those cakes and feel sad? And why am I so certain, when I am only eleven years old, that no matter how many years go by, I will never be able to look at this picture and laugh.

The Valentine cakes

Theater of Romance

*I*t's Friday night, and Mama is home from work early. My father always cooks on Friday nights, but this night he sits at the kitchen table and reads the newspaper.

I am reading, too. Not a schoolbook or a book from the library, but a story that I'm writing. Mr. O'Neil says that the best way to get good at anything is to do it over and over. "Practice makes perfect," he says. I figure that if I want to be a writer when I grow up, I should start practicing now.

The name of my story is "Carefree Caress."

"Don't you love the title?" I ask Rose when I printed it on a clean sheet of white paper. "Isn't it great alliteration?"

"What's the story going to be about?" Rose asked.

I told her it was a secret, because I didn't know for sure. I knew it would be a love story, but I didn't know who the characters would be. I couldn't write about high school, because the only thing I know about high school is stuff I read in books. And that would be copying. So I sat and thought about what I did know, and then I began to write.

Mama says, "It's really wonderful that you're writing, Beverly." I think it's wonderful, too. I carry a notebook everywhere, like a real writer, and jot things down as I think of them; like if the sky looks extra pretty, I'll write, "The sky is as blue as food coloring today." And I'll use that later.

I have six pages done on my story, but now I'm stuck. I don't know where to go next. This girl Sandra, named after Sandra Singer, is in love with William, named after Mr. O'Neil. They go to movies and dances, hold hands and kiss in the back of William's father's car. Then one day William tells Sandra that he can't see her anymore.

"Why not?" she asks him. "Don't you still love me?"

"Of course I love you, Sandra. But I've decided I am going to become a priest."

Sandra cries and cries. "Why are you going to leave

me and become a priest?"

"Because God has called me," William declares.

William doesn't see Sandra for three whole weeks. Then, the night before he is to go away to the seminary — which is where boys go to become priests — he telephones Sandra. "I have to see you one last time," he begs. "I want you to meet me in the woods in an hour."

"I can't go into the woods with you," Sandra sobs. "You're going to be a priest."

"But I'm not a priest yet," William replies.

It's right here that I'm stuck. Now what can I have William and Sandra do?

Mama's fish cakes are not as good as my father's. It's funny because Mama buys them at the A&P in a package, and all my father does is fry them in a pan. That's exactly what she does, too, but for some reason, his taste better.

But Mama's desserts are the best. Sometimes on Friday nights after dinner my father will hand me a quarter and say, "Why don't you run over to Gilroy's and get us some ice cream?" But Mama makes desserts, cupcakes and cookies. We have chocolate cupcakes tonight. We eat them hot from the oven, with confectioners' sugar sprinkled on the top.

Mama sips her coffee and says, "Why don't you read us some of what you've written, Beverly." And my father nods and says, "That's a great idea."

"It's not finished yet," I tell them. "It's not even half done."

I'm not sure this is the truth. It may be more than half done. It may be all done. I don't know. But I think if I read it to them, maybe they'll help me decide what I should write next.

So I read. I sit in my father's seat because he says, "Sit here, the light's better." He sits in my seat, and Mama sits where she always sits and drinks her coffee and smokes a cigarette while I read the entire six pages without stopping. When I get to the end, where William says, "But I'm not a priest yet," I look up.

"That's it," I say. "That's all I have done."

My parents are silent. I think maybe they didn't hear me, so I repeat, "That's all I have done."

"Well, your story is certainly interesting," my father says, after clearing his throat. "I have just one question: Where did you come up with the idea of a boy meeting a girl in the woods?"

"I made it up, Dad. It's a good idea, don't you think?"

"Do you know any girls who meet boys in the woods?"

"No. It's just a story. It's make-believe. Do you like it?"

"Well, you had to get the idea from somewhere," Mama says. "Is this what you're learning at school?"

I think, maybe they don't like it. Maybe they think it's an awful story. Is it stupid? Did I do a bad job writing it? Maybe there's too much alliteration.

My father turns to my mother and says, "I don't think she understands what she's written." My mother says, "I knew we should have kept her in Catholic school." I say, so they'll stop talking about me as if I'm not in the room, "Want me to help you with the dishes, Mama?"

Mama says, "No. That's OK." And my father says, "Can I take a look at that story?" and I hand it to him.

Shane and I go outside. It's dark and cold, and the sky is full of stars. That's what I should write next: "They meet in the woods. It's dark and cold, and the sky is full of stars."

I go back inside, ask my father for my story, take it upstairs and continue to write.

Three Steps to Heaven

I might not be going to the junior high school next year. My mother and father want to send me to Catholic school. They never talked about a Catholic school before I read them "Carefree Caress," but now it's all they talk about. They say it has nothing to do with "Carefree Caress." They say that they don't want me on double sessions again next year, that I am not learning as much as I should.

But I am. I'm learning a lot. I get practically all A's on my report card. I read all the time. I don't want to leave my friends, Mama. I don't want to leave Rose.

Mama says I won't be leaving Rose, that even if I go to a different school, I'll still see her on weekends and vacations. Plus I'll make new friends, she says.

But I don't want to make new friends. I like my old friends.

I have to take a test to see if I'm smart enough to go to a Catholic school. Mama takes the day off from work and drives to St. Mark's in Dorchester, which is a long drive from home. She parks on a narrow street that looks like Calvin Street, except it doesn't curve. But the houses are the same: three-deckers with porches in the back.

Mama walks me to the door of the brick school and rings a bell. A sister answers, and Mama explains why we're here. The sister nods, and Mama says, "I'll wait for you in the car, Baybo." I follow the sister into the cold, dark building. The only sounds I hear are our footsteps and her rosary beads clicking.

I take the test alone. Everyone else has already taken it. The deadline is past. But the sisters have made an exception for me, Mama explained.

I don't want to be an exception. I don't want to be here in this big, cold, empty room with Sister looking at me. But then Sister smiles and says, "Don't worry, dear. It's not a hard test. Just relax, and you'll do fine."

Sister is right. It isn't hard. Rosemary and I play school all the time, and we make up much harder tests. I finish it quickly and hand it to the sister, and she walks me to the door.

I remember to say, "Thank you, Sister," because I know it's important to be polite. She smiles again and says, "I hope to see you soon, Beverly." I nod and run across the street to where my mother is waiting.

"Don't tell anyone about taking the test," Mama says.

"Why not?" I ask.

"It's better to wait and see if you get in. Then you can tell."

But I have to tell Rose. How can I not tell? And why shouldn't I? I don't want to go to Catholic school anyway.

So I phone her. She says, "Where were you today? Are you sick? How come you weren't in school?"

I tell her where I was, making her swear not to tell anyone else. She says, "You shouldn't have tried on the test. You should have written down all the wrong answers if you really didn't want to go."

She's right. I should have pretended I was stupid. Why didn't I?

Easter arrives. I wear nylons, a blue flowered skirt, a white blouse and a small white hat that Mama borrowed from Wethern's. Father Finn says Mass, and on the way home in the car, I eat a Fanny Farmer butter cream Easter egg.

The Nanas, Aunt Lorraine and Uncle Frank come to dinner. Aunt Lorraine is having another baby. She's wearing a royal blue skirt and a blue and white smock because her dresses don't fit. Even with her stomach sticking out, Aunt Lorraine is beautiful.

Mama doesn't say anything about Aunt Lorraine getting another baby, but I think she must be sad. I would be. I'm sad every time Rose gets a better mark than I do, even though I love Rose. I try just as hard as she does, but she always beats me anyway. I wonder if Mama feels as if Aunt Lorraine is beating her.

I wear my Easter outfit to the sixth-grade dance —

everything but the hat — and I paint my fingernails blue to match my skirt. Diane Hyman wears a grey skirt and a pink sweater. She walks to my house because my father is driving us. He says we look very pretty and makes us pose for a picture in our front yard before we go.

When we arrive, Janet, Ann Marie and Rose, and most all the girls are dancing with other girls. The boys aren't dancing at all. The music is loud, the lights are bright and the place is crowded. I think every sixth-grader in Randolph must be here. I look for George and there he is in a crowd of boys across the room. He looks nice. Handsome. All the boys look nice in their jackets and ties.

But it takes them until almost the end of the dance to come out of their corners. All night they rock back and forth on their feet, and they talk only to one another. Even when there's a ladies' choice, they don't look as if they want to dance. A few do, the ones Sandra Singer asks, but most bolt when a girl approaches, as if they all of a sudden remember that they have something important to do off the dance floor.

Twenty minutes before the dance is supposed to end, they finally cross over to the girls' side. It's as if a bell has rung somewhere that only the boys hear. "Dream" is on the record player, a cha-cha, but they must think it's a slow song because that's what they do. They dance slow.

"In the night when I want you, to hold me tight, whenever I want you, all I have to do is dre-e-e-eam, dream, dream, dre-eam, dre-e-e-eam, dream, dream, dream."

I wait for George Falcone to ask me to dance. I cross my fingers and toes. But George doesn't dance with anyone. He stands on his side of the room, and I stand on mine. Diane and I cha-cha together. Mr. Hyman drives us home. "Did you have a good time?" he asks. We nod and giggle, because we really, really did. It didn't matter that the boys didn't dance with us. We had fun anyway.

"I can't wait for the next dance," I say.

"Neither can I," Diane says back.

Grade 6 — Tower Hill School

Mr. O'Neil   *Debbie Barnes*   *Judy Bouzan*

Stanley Burwell   *Beverly Curtin*   *Diane Hyman*   *Rosemary Jablonski*

Patricia Lebrocquy *Anne Marie Lipus* *Michael Ryan* *Ann Marie Tantillo*

Prize Performance

*M*r. O'Neil takes us to the Museum of Science. The whole class goes, but Rose and I get to ride to Cambridge with him.

We sit in the back seat, and we are as good as gold. We don't giggle. We don't sing. We don't whisper under our breath things that we don't want Mr. O'Neil to hear. We're polite. We listen to the radio, and when Mr. O'Neil talks, we listen to him.

There's a boy in the front seat from Miss Kelly's class. I don't know why Miss Kelly's kids didn't go with her or with their own mothers. But things got confused, so we have this boy we don't know in Mr. O'Neil's car with us. That's OK. Mr. O'Neil talks to him. They talk about baseball.

At the museum we're assigned to a group that we're supposed to stay with. But if we get separated we're to meet at two o'clock sharp in the gift shop, Mr. O'Neil says. Rose and I get separated from the group immediately. We head for the big room with all the telephones that talk to you and tell you how they work. Then we race to the space exhibit, to the cafeteria and to the Transparent Woman.

We're not supposed to go there. That's what Mr. O'Neil said. "We're not going to the Transparent Woman, because this exhibit is for older children."

Rose and I go anyway. The Transparent Woman is naked and clear plastic. You can see her outsides and her insides. We learn about pelvic bones, fallopian tubes, ovaries, the uterus and breasts.

In the gift shop I look at a model of the transparent woman and try to find the uterus. I can't, but Rose does. She wants to pool the money that our mothers gave us to buy souvenirs, and buy the model and learn all about the human body instead. But I want to buy a key chain of Jupiter.

On the way home from the museum, Rose and I get the giggles because it's late in the afternoon, we're tired, it's spring, and sixth grade is going to be over soon. We'll probably never see Mr. O'Neil again. Rose will be at the junior high, which is way uptown, and I'll be in Dorchester, which is part of Boston and far away. So I won't see anyone, ever.

So we whisper and giggle, then tell Mr. O'Neil that we want to sing a song that we wrote about him.

"Are you sure you want to sing it, girls?" he says.

"Sure, we're sure." Then we begin. We sing the whole thing, from start to finish:

"Mr. O'Neil is a guy who can steal, any heart, any place, any time. Mr. O'Neil came home one night from stealing another teacher's wife. He wasn't living very long, and now we remember him by this song."

Mr. O'Neil's neck and ears turn bright red. He laughs and laughs. When he drops us off at my house — Rosemary is staying over — he gets out of the car, opens our door, bows like a prince and says, "Next year won't be the same without you girls."

•　•　•　•

There's a letter from St. Mark's in the mailbox. I open it. "Congratulations!" it says.

I don't want to go to St. Mark's. I don't want to go to St. Mark's more than anything in the world. I wish I could tear up the letter and flush it down the toilet. What would happen if I did? Who would know?

I sit in the parlor holding the thin, white paper, which I could light with a match and burn. I think about next year, how I won't know anyone at school, how when lunch time comes there won't be anyone to sit with, and how Rose will be with all our friends. She'll have a new best friend, and I won't have anyone.

I put the letter back in the envelope, walk into the kitchen and prop it up against the sugar bowl.

And then I walk to Rose's to give her the bad news.

•　•　•　•

The last day of sixth grade is the saddest thing,

because I know I won't see Philip Angeleri or Patricia Lebrocquy or Anne Marie Lipus ever again. They don't live anywhere near where I live, and I won't see them next year in school.

I have been assigned to the accelerated class with Rose and Diane. I go home and show my mother the notice and beg her, "Please, please, can't I go to the junior high school now? I'll be with Rose in all her classes, and with Diane, and she's smart, too. I'd try so hard. I'd get all A's. I know I would."

But Mama says, "No Beverly. It's decided. You're going to St. Mark's."

Michael Ryan is going to St. Mark's, too, but he's not my friend, so he doesn't count. I'm not going to have any friends next year. I'm going to be all alone.

• • • •

Rosemary gets a babysitting job for the summer. Every day she has to take care of this little boy, David. She has to walk to his house in the morning, put him in his carriage, take him to her house and play with him. She gets a quarter an hour, a dollar a day, five dollars a week. She is going to be rich.

I have to go into Boston to be measured for a school uniform, even though I just got out of school, even though it's a Wednesday, it's hot, and it's a perfect day to go to the beach.

Mama drives to Forest Hills and parks the car. We take the train into the city. We walk straight to Arch Street and light a candle. Then we eat at Colestone's, just as we always do. Even though it's hot, I have macaroni and cheese. Then I go to get measured. A lady with thin, grey hair like Big Nana's measures my shoulders, waist, hips and legs. She writes all the numbers down on an index card. She tells Mama the uniform will be ready in eight weeks, and it will be mailed to us.

I look at the sample hanging on a rack. It's an ugly thing, a shiny green jumper that will make my breasts look even bigger than they are because you have to wear this ugly white blouse under it and an ugly green bow tie. My mother orders two blouses, one jumper and one bow tie. I think about how much fun school shopping used to be, and how when I can finally wear nylons and shoes without straps, I have to wear long socks and uniform shoes that tie.

I see Rose mostly on weekends now because she's busy with David during weekdays. Sometimes I babysit with her, but it's not fun. David cries, and Rose has to hold him, feed him, walk him, change him or something. Sometimes we walk him all the way to the Dairy Queen, and that's fun. But Rose says it isn't, because it's a way longer walk for her than for me.

On Saturdays we still go to the bakery, the library and the movies. Sometimes Rose buys me a Charleston Chew or Peggy Lawton chocolate chip cookies to go with my lime rickey because she's rich now. On Sundays we still sit under our tree at the School for the Deaf.

We've finally figured out the baby thing, the whole thing this time, though it's hard to believe that people do what Grace Winters told Rose they do. But Rose says Grace wasn't lying. "Who would make up a thing like that?" Rose says. Grace said that the sixth commandment is all about this, too. That's why when you ask grownups what adultery is, they never tell you. They don't like to talk about intercourse, Grace said.

• • • •

Mama told me about Santa Claus, too. I think I knew all along, but I needed her to say the words.

I waited until before church one Sunday. We were in the car in the parking lot, Mama about to open the door, when I said, "I have to ask you a question, Mama." She turned, and I thought, my mother is so pretty. She was wearing a black felt hat trimmed with mink "borrowed" from Wethern's.

"Mama, you have to tell me the truth because if you

don't, you won't be able to go to Communion, and then I'll know anyway," I said.

I had it figured out. If Mama said there is a Santa and then didn't go to Communion, I'd know she lied. If she said there is a Santa and walked up to the altar rail, I'd know there is a Santa, and that my friends are wrong.

I took a deep breath.

"Are you Santa, Mama? Do you buy the gifts?"

Mama's face crumpled like a mirror in a cowboy movie when a bullet hits it.

"I didn't mean to lie to you, Beverly. It's just that Christmas isn't the same when you don't believe in Santa. That's why I didn't tell you. I didn't want to be the one to ruin your Christmases."

"It's OK, Mama," I said. "Really, don't cry. You didn't ruin my Christmases. I knew before you told me. Honest."

And the truth is I did.

• • • •

It's a weekday, and Rose is babysitting for David. My mother and father are at work, I've already made a bowl of blue cereal and eaten it so I can tell Rose that she's wrong about blue cereal. Rose has this theory that the reason cereals and things like Hostess cupcakes aren't blue is because people don't like blue food. I think blue food is just fine. Yesterday, I drank a blue milk shake. Today, I put blue food coloring on my Rice Krispies. Tomorrow, I am going to dye an egg white blue.

I call Rose to tell her what I did, but Mrs. Jablonski says that Rose and Grace just left to walk David home. Rose has been spending a lot of time with Grace lately because Grace doesn't mind having to share Rose with David. I don't like to share Rose with anyone.

I have nothing to do, so I decide to look in my mother's bureau drawer where she keeps all the old pictures. That's always fun. It's hot, but it's cool in her room. I can hear the little kids next door playing tag, and I think, how come Janet, Ann Marie and I don't play tag anymore?

I look through the El Producto cigar box at pictures of people I don't know and at pictures of my mother and father taken before I knew them. Most I've seen before. But some I've forgotten I've seen. I like looking at my father's army pictures best.

When I say to him, "What did you do in the war, Dad?" he says, "I don't want to talk about the war." He never talks about the war. I look at a picture of him in a uniform standing with another guy next to a truck, and I think my father is so handsome. All my friends think he's handsome, too, so it's not just my opinion. I think he was even more handsome when he was young.

There's printing on the back of the picture in my father's neat, big letters: VINCENT VELLUCCI — LARRY CURTIN — SARDINIA.

I look up Sardinia in the unabridged dictionary, which my father keeps on the floor next to his desk in his office.

"**Sar-din-i-a** — *n.* a large island in the Mediterranean, west of Italy: with small nearby islands it comprises a department of Italy."

I didn't know that my father had been to Italy. I don't know much about my father, really, except that he works all the time, and when he's not working, he's studying to be sergeant, fixing TVs, cutting the grass or driving to Cambridge to get the Nanas.

I wonder if Vinnie Vellucci was my father's best friend, the way first Theresa, then Mary Andrews, was my mother's best friend. I wonder if boy best friends are like girl best friends and tell each other almost everything. I wish I could ask my father this. I wish I had a brother so I knew more about boys and how they think.

I go to put the cigar box back because it's almost time for this new show, "American Bandstand," which is just great. It's a bunch of kids dancing to all these cool songs. I've been watching it every afternoon for almost a week now. I place the box exactly where it was and am about to close the drawer when I see a small envelope stuck to the side of the drawer.

I take it out, open it, and there's my father's printing again. Only this time his printing isn't on the back of a picture, it's on stationery, and it isn't just two names and a place, it's a poem.

"Because of you dear, I am so blue
Because to me your love was not true
You left me without even a good-bye
And in my heart there is nothing but a sigh.
I know, dear, that I am far away
With time on your hands you are bound to stray
For I am no longer in your view
And there is another now dear to you.
I thought while in a foreign land
A place where no one understands
That I could always turn to you
But as this is gone, dear we are through.
I don't want to blame you this is true
For finding another to be close to you.
But I will adore you for eternity.
And you will forever be part of me."

Did my father write this? It's his printing. I didn't know he could write poetry. Who did he write this to?

It's in my mother's drawer. Was it to her? Did he write these words when he was in Sardinia? Was she in love with someone else, and did she change her mind and remember how she loved him after she read this?

I have so many questions that I don't bother with "American Bandstand." I tear a piece of paper out of my notebook and copy all the words, then put the poem back in the envelope in the drawer. Then I call Rosemary again. This time she answers, and I tell her what I found.

She reads the poem. The real one. The one in the drawer. She's come to my house. She said she wanted to see the real thing. "I can't believe your father wrote this," she says. "Are you sure he did?"

How can I be sure? It's his writing, but maybe he

copied it from a book. It's good enough to be from a book. But then why would my mother have saved it?

Rose says, lowering her voice as if my father is in the next room, "Maybe your mother had another boyfriend."

But I don't think so. She never loved anyone but my father. That's what she's told me.

"Why don't you ask your father?" Rose says.

But we both know I can't do that.

We put the poem back in the drawer and straighten the bed where we were sitting. When my father comes home he finds us upstairs in my room on the floor playing Monopoly.

"And are you girls having a good day?" he asks.

"Just fine, Dad."

"A great day, Mr. Curtin," Rose says. "Thank you for asking."

We send the poem to Crown Music Company because there is an ad in *Photoplay*: "Poems Wanted — We'll turn your poem into a song." We're positive that this poem is so romantic that it will be a huge hit song and then my father will be rich and famous. When he is, he'll say, "And it's all because of you girls."

I ask Rose to copy "Because of You" onto plain white paper, because her handwriting with the small O's for dots is prettier than mine. We put the poem in a white envelope to the attention of Larry Allen, who is the director of Crown Publishing Company, and write Rose's address in the corner. We don't want the answer coming to my house. I want this to be a big surprise.

I think about what it will be like to hear my father's song on the radio. I wonder if Perry Como will sing it. I hope he does. I wonder if we'll move to a bigger house when we're rich. Maybe then, the record people will hear Mama sing, and she'll be famous, too, since everyone already says she sounds just like Rosemary Clooney. She'll be happy singing; she'll be so busy performing in nightclubs and shows and on TV that she won't be sad

Beverly Beckham

anymore. When people meet her on the street they'll say, "You have the most beautiful voice, Dorothy," and, "We really enjoyed your show." And no one, not even old friends, will ask, "How many children do you have?"

March of Time

My school uniform arrives wrinkled, and Mama irons it on the wrong side so the iron doesn't make it shiny. "This is how you have to iron it, Beverly," she says. She irons the blouses, too, creasing the sleeves the way my father creases his uniform sleeves, and then says, "Why don't you try it on to make sure it fits."

It doesn't. It's too small at the top. They measured wrong. I can't even zipper it, and school starts next week.

Maybe I won't have to go to St. Mark's after all. "I can't go if I don't have a uniform, Mama."

She calls the uniform place, and they tell her to take my measurements again and send the uniform back. They'll make me another one, but it won't be ready for at least two weeks.

"But school starts next week. I can't go without a uniform," I insist.

Mama calls the school. The Mother Superior says, "Send her without a uniform. Just send her. She can't miss school." So on the first day, I wear a plaid dress.

See. There I am with Michael Ryan posing for the camera. It's funny how we're both smiling when we're not even happy. Neither of us wants to go to St. Mark's in Dorchester, which is ten miles away. We want to stay in Randolph with our friends.

My parents are going to drive us to school every day. Mama will get up early, make breakfast, take the pin curls out of her hair and sit in the passenger seat while my father drives me to Dorchester. Then she'll drive him to the MDC police station at Blue Hills in Milton and drop him there. Then she'll go home, clean up, dress up and go to work in Quincy. Every afternoon, I'll take the bus home, my father will hitch a ride, and my mother will drive. She won't get home until after six o'clock because her work lasts the longest.

It's seven o'clock in the morning when we get to Dorchester, and school doesn't start until 8:30, but we have to get here early because my father has to be at work before eight, and my mother at nine. This is the way it is.

Michael Ryan goes for a walk. I go to church. It's a big, old, dark church that smells like winter and wax, even on a late summer day. But I love church, even this unfamiliar one. I don't mind being alone here.

After church, I walk over to the schoolyard, but no one is there yet. When the kids start to arrive, no one talks to me. The girls play on one side of the yard, the boys on the other, like back at St. Joseph's. When the bell rings, the girls line up separately from the boys. I follow the girls into the building. We file up ramps, not steps, in silence on opposite sides of each other.

Sister Ellen St. Dennis is tall, thin and very serious looking, but she seems nice. She introduces me to the class. "This is Beverly Curtin," she says. "She's new this year. Please stand, Beverly," she says, and I do. Some of the kids smile. Some stare at me.

The classroom is old and dark like the church and the windows are big rectangles that make the outside look shimmery like in a dream. Some of the windows are open, so you can hear the outside. I hear cars, trucks, ambulances and a clock that chimes every fifteen minutes. We kneel on our chairs, close our eyes and say the "Morning Offering," then the rosary with Archbishop Cushing. The clock chimes once.

After prayers we have religion. It isn't like religion at Sunday school, where we have to answer questions in a book. Sister tells us stories about people who have dedicated their lives to God, like Father Damien and Dr. Tom Dooley, and she reads us things that they wrote and things that were written about them. Then we have arithmetic, and that's hard; then spelling; then English, and that's even harder. Then we kneel again and say the "Blessing Before Meals," and then we have lunch.

Almost all the kids go home for lunch. Children who can't go home because they live too far away or because they don't have mothers at home have to stay in the school hall and eat. Lunch is from 11:30 to 1:00. It takes ten minutes to eat; then you have to sit and wait until the bell rings; then you go outside and hang around the schoolyard. Some of the kids who sit and wait know each other and whisper. I know Michael, but he's a boy, so he sits at a separate table.

After lunch we pray again, the "Grace After Meals" and the "Acts of Faith, Hope and Love." Then we have geography, then penmanship. My penmanship is awful because first I was taught the Palmer method, then the Rhinehart method, and now I have to write the Palmer method again. Everyone in the whole room has beautiful handwriting except me. Sister gives me a blue book to take home and fill with straight lines and curly O's.

Before class is dismissed, we kneel and pray for the final time. We say "The Angelus" and "Hail Holy Queen."

I have to walk to Ashmont Station to get the bus home. Michael Ryan doesn't come with me. He walks to the school where his father teaches. He'll wait and go home with him every day. It's about a mile walk to Ashmont. Then it's a twenty-five-minute bus ride to Randolph. Then it's another mile up Chestnut Street to my house. My book bag is heavy, I'm hot and hungry, and it's 4:15 when I get home.

Shane jumps on me, then charges outside. I pour a glass of milk, grab a handful of chocolate chip cookies, and look at all my books that need to be covered, opened and studied. I ignore them and call Rose.

Mrs. Jablonski answers. "How was your day? Do you like your new school?" she asks. I lie and say, "It's fine, thank you." And she says, "The first day is always the hardest." I don't say anything — what can I say? Then she says, "Rose isn't home yet. But I'm expecting her any minute. I'll have her call the second she gets in."

I leave my books on the kitchen table, grab some more cookies, pour another glass of milk, turn on "American

Bandstand" and wait for Rosemary to call.

On my second day of seventh grade, I wear a peach dress that I think looks nice, and I go to Mass again. After Mass I walk across the street and buy an orange soda and a glazed donut, and wait until it's almost time for the bell to ring before I head for the schoolyard. I cross the street with a boy I recognize from my room. I smile at him and say, "Hi." He says, "Nice dress. Where'd you get it? The Salvation Army?"

At lunch I file out of school with all the kids so I don't have to sit at a table in the school hall by myself. I don't have a home to go to, but I pretend that I do. For an hour-and-a-half, I walk around the neighborhood. I discover Codman Square.

When my uniform arrives I put it on and wear it to school. Now I look like everyone else. But I still don't fit in. Michael Ryan stops coming to school because his parents decide to let him go to Randolph Junior High School. I wonder what he said to make them change their minds. I ask him, and he shrugs.

It's not all that bad, though, not really. I mean I like some of it. I like church, religion and all the prayers. And I love Gregorian chant. I think, maybe, I might not be a writer when I grow up. I might be a nun.

Rose says, "Don't be ridiculous, Beverly. You're always changing what you're going to be." But I'm not being ridiculous. I'm serious.

Sister says that sometimes when God loves people very much he gives them the stigmata. The stigmata is when you bleed from your palms and your feet like Jesus did on the cross. In church every morning, I pray for the stigmata. I don't pray please, please, please, God. Sister says you have to say, "Thy will be done," when you pray for things like the stigmata. But Rose says that the stigmata is like Elaine Maganello's doll poop, just a made-up story, and what's wrong with me anyway?

Sometimes at lunch I go to church and say an extra

prayer for the stigmata. But most times I walk up to Codman Square and go to the library. The librarian there is so nice. She lets me get any book I want, even if it's in the adult section. Sometimes she has a book waiting for me, like "Out of My Darkness," by William Shepard.

Once in a while on Fridays, if I haven't had a donut every morning and I've managed to save enough money, I buy lunch at Colestone's, which is right across the street from the library. I get macaroni and cheese, and I sit at a small table and eat and read.

Sometimes, when I'm alone and pretending not to be lonely, I wonder what Rose is doing for lunch. I think of her with Grace Winters and Regina Kalitsis, a new friend she talks about all the time. I think about Val Poche, a boy she likes, a boy I don't even know. I think about how there are so many things I don't know now about Rose and so many things she doesn't know now about me, like how I eat lunch alone sometimes, and how when I'm standing at the chalkboard trying to diagram a sentence and the kids are laughing softly at me and Sister is saying, "Don't be rude, boys and girls. She's new, and this is difficult, and she's doing so well," I wish I could die.

I think how it's different now, because I'm different. I don't have any friends. There's a girl named Carol and she's nice. Barbara, Dottie and Kathy smile at me, and I smile back. Sometimes we even talk, but it's not the same. They're just being nice. They don't really like me.

Mama keeps saying give it time. So I'm giving everything time: my handwriting, my diagramming, my parsing of verbs, my quest for the stigmata and new friends, even my father's poem. In time even that will work out.

We heard back from Crown Publishers. They sent us a contract. "Whereas Beverly Curtin is the author and sole owner of the song poem entitled 'Because of You'; and Whereas, the author wishes the collaboration of Crown Music Company; Now, therefore, Crown Music Company agrees to compose music to said song poem." The only thing is they want seventy-five dollars. It might as well be seventy-five million.

Where are we going to get seventy-five dollars, I ask Rose, while walking downtown.

She says she doesn't know, but we'll figure out something. She thinks maybe we should ask my father for some of the money because it's his poem, isn't it? But I want it to be a surprise.

Maybe we'll babysit a lot or do another Minstrel Show. Maybe I'll stop getting an orange soda and a donut every morning. I mean I could. "Maybe we should give up the movies, Rose."

"Not the movies," she says, stopping dead in her tracks. "We can never give up the movies."

I look at her and understand. The movies are our connection, the one thing that hasn't changed ever. Here it is, Saturday, and here we are, our pockets stuffed with change just as they always are every Saturday, St. Mark's, Val Poche and even the stigmata very far away.

After the movies we'll go to the drugstore and sit on the high stools. I'll have a regular lime rickey, and Rose will have a raspberry lime rickey, "with plain water," she'll say, because that's how she likes them now. We'll split a package of Peggy Lawton chocolate chip cookies, and we'll talk about what we saw, what we liked, how we feel and what we think. For all the time we're together it won't matter that we go to different schools and have different friends and that every day gone is one day closer to our being more different than we are the same.

I wish today would never end, I say to Rose after the movies, when we are on our way home. It's light still, and we're walking and talking. We just saw "This Happy Feeling," with Debbie Reynolds. "I could laugh, I could cry, I could float through the sky, what a happy, happy feeling," we sing in loud, happy voices, because no one can hear us. Because we're all alone.

"Eddie Fisher's a jerk, don't you think?" Rose says.

"He a real jerk. Plus, he can't even sing."

We sing "Tammy" then, and we sing it, not separately, the way we usually do, but together, arm in arm, walking as close as we can, as if we're playing "Anybody in my way gets a five-cent boot."

Which, in fact, we are.

Me and Rosemary

Epilogue

*A*nd life went on. I read a book a week all through seventh and eighth grade. I said more prayers in two years than I would say in the next thirty. I wrote a poem, "Prayer to Our Lord," and it was published in a religious anthology somewhere in the South. I ate a lot of chocolate chip cookies and kept trying to fit in. I never did.

The summer between seventh and eight grade, Rose and I stopped talking. I promised that if she walked from her house to mine to go to the Dairy Queen with me, I'd buy her a banana split. But when we got there I had just enough money for a cone. It wasn't because of the ice cream that she was angry. It was because I lied.

We made up in November on her thirteenth birthday. I called and said, "Happy Birthday, Rose. I miss you." And she took a deep breath and said she missed me, too. We've been friends since.

I still see Diane once in a while. She lives a few miles from where we grew up. I see Janet when she flies home from California, and I talk to Ann Marie and Michelle every now and then.

George Falcone is married and has ten children.

Father Finn is still a priest and lives in South Boston.

My father made sergeant, and my mother sewed his stripes on his uniform. When I finally asked him about "Because of You," he told me that the men in his company used to pay him to write poetry for them. This one he had written for Vinnie Vellucci. Crown Publishing Company never turned his poem into a song because we never came up with the seventy-five dollars.

My mother left Wethern's and went to work selling hats at Sheridan's at South Shore Plaza, one of the first shopping malls. My father left the police force and went into real estate.

Little Nana died in a fire. Big Nana died of cancer.

Aunt Lorraine had six children, five girls and a boy.

My mother never had any more children. I was her only one.

About the Author

*A*mong the thorny, opinionated op/ed pages of *The Boston Herald* blooms a writer of hope, empathy and quiet moments. Like a good friend, Beverly Beckham uses words like neighborly and kindness. She writes about people we all know, about family and friends, about holidays and ordinary days, about our daily struggles and many accomplishments, and gently reminds us to take a look at our lives and smile.

Beverly Beckham is an award-winning columnist and editorial writer for *The Boston Herald*, the second-largest daily newspaper in New England. Beckham is also the author of "A Gift of Time," a collection of personal essays, as well as a contributor to "A 6th Bowl of Chicken Soup for the Soul®" and "A Second Chicken Soup for the Woman's Soul®."

Beckham began her writing career in 1979. Her articles and essays have appeared in newspapers and magazines in the United States and Canada. She is a frequent guest on radio and TV, as well as a keynote speaker for women's clubs and organizations nationwide.

She lives in Canton, Massachusetts, with her husband of 32 years. They have three grown children.